CONE-BEARING TREES OF THE
PACIFIC COAST

Typical of the aged bristlecone pine is a small but healthy remnant of live branches.

(Color negative by Edwin C. Rockwell, Jr.)

CONE-BEARING TREES

OF THE

PACIFIC COAST

BY

NATHAN A. BOWERS

B.Sc., C.E., Ph.D., D.Eng.

SEVENTH PRINTING

*In which is included new material
on the oldest known living things*

PACIFIC BOOKS

Publishers

Palo Alto, California

Library of Congress Catalog Card Number: 56–9436

Printed and bound in the United States of America

PREFACE

In its original form the material in this manual was prepared as a convenient means of helping the author get better acquainted with cone-bearing trees of Pacific forests. Then he discovered that there were others, by no means botanists, who loved the forest trees and needed help in learning more about them. The common difficulty was a lack of effective aids. It seems strange that so little information is prepared for the nonbotanical lover of trees, this despite the many years in which scientists have been studying our forests, classifying the trees, and making painstaking and exhaustive records of what and where they are—all for those who understand botanical terms.

There is a need, the author believes, for something in between the technical treatise and the sketchy "popular" material that does not at all reflect the very exhaustive information locked up in technical records. Even though one was neither a botanist nor interested in a knowledge of botanical terminology, he still could know a great deal about trees, know their characteristic traits, learn to recognize them on sight, and find much pleasure in a close acquaintance with them. Was there not some way in which the information in the scientific records could be made available to the nonbotanical tree lover and thus help him attain this nontechnical and yet close acquaintance with the trees? In short, could not a field manual on conifers native to Pacific Coast forests be made comprehensive and definite without making it technical in a botanical sense?

To produce an affirmative answer to these questions was the task that the author set for himself in preparing the material here presented. He believes that there are many tree lovers who want and will use a manual made as comprehensive and complete as possible without botanical terms. This manual is designed to meet that need, and at the same time it is kept within the limits of what would be useful on mountain trips and in ramblings through forests of the Pacific slope.

This manual would not have been complete and would have fallen far short of the objective without the drawings of needles and cones for each species that originally appeared in "Forest Trees of the Pacific Slope" by George B. Sudworth, dendrologist, U.S. Forest Service. The author gratefully acknowledges the help of the Forest Service not only in preparing these drawings for reproduction but in supplying photographs of many species.

John A. Lee of Portland, by his own diligent study of trees and his persevering effort to get together information that the layman could understand and use in identification, was an inspiring influence as well as an unfailing source of encouragement. He also supplied numerous ideas and special methods useful in identification. These results of his own careful and observant study have not been published heretofore. Much credit, therefore, is due Mr. Lee and is gratefully acknowledged.

George D. Whittle made special effort, over a period of years, to obtain representative pictures of tree species that were not otherwise readily available. Botanist John Thomas Howell of the Academy of Sciences supplied much helpful advice with reference to all parts of the manual and assembled all the data on the cypresses.

To numerous other friends who have contributed from their personal collections pictures that were not available elsewhere, the author expresses his thanks and appreciation.

Nathan A. Bowers

The Sequoias
Portola Valley, California

PREFACE TO THE SEVENTH PRINTING

U NLIKE manufactured products, which too often present "new models" from year to year, trees have traits and characteristics which do not change—at least not within a human lifetime. A means of identification or a system for recognizing the different species does not get out of date quickly and, if it is good and sufficient, needs no revision from year to year. Fortunately more than twenty years of field use has demonstrated the effectiveness of the system used in this manual for identification of conifer species.

The seventh printing, therefore, again presents the same systematic identification by a process of elimination, which is now republished with the confidence born of long and successful application in the field.

Although there is nothing to be added to the methods for identifying species, there is another phase of the study of trees which has for years engrossed the attention of the author and which he would like to share with others. This is the study of tree rings. It can be taken up by any one who cares to carry his study of our forest trees a little further than mere identification of species, getting below the surface, as it were, to learn something of tree ages, rates of growth, and the curious ways in which nature works with trees.

If such a study at first seems too technical or likely to involve too much time and effort, let it be said that it offers intriguing rewards. It is not necessary for one actually to do the work of counting annual rings on a redwood stump, examine the freshly sawed end of a piece of construction timber, or polish the cross section of a branch from an interesting tree. He can leave these things to others and still derive much information from, and find delightful diversion in, a casual acquaintance with modern progress and development in the science of tree-ring study and the dating of tree growth. Even a little time devoted to this science —known as dendrochronology—will open new vistas.

Therefore in adding to the fifth printing a chapter devoted to Tree-Ring Analysis, the author offered no apology. For those who desire aid only in identifying species of native conifers, the book still provides all that was available before. For those who may wish to experiment somewhat on their own account, it is hoped that the material there presented will afford sufficient information to enable them to make at least the preliminary tests and studies that lead to age and growth-rate determinations. Beyond that point there is no limit to the further pursuit of a hobby which might well result from an application of the simple rules and suggestions.

In the sixth printing a section of sixteen pages was added, picturing and describing "inspirational trees" that have survived in spite of natural handicaps, and which can well be an inspiration to man.

Finally, since the sixth printing appeared, much additional work has been done on determining the age of the bristlecone pines which grow at high elevations where the growing season is very short and nature seems to be most inhospitable. It has been determined through several years of painstaking research that these trees are the oldest known living things. This new information appears for the first time in this seventh printing.

NATHAN A. BOWERS

The Sequoias
Portola Valley, California
January, 1965

CONTENTS

FOREWORD TO FIFTH PRINTING

By Waldo S. Glock *

The study of tree rings has gone far in recent years. As application of botanical sciences and methods has been made, new aspects have developed and by degrees it has become possible to unravel some of the mysteries and certainly to reach a better understanding of fundamentals. The study of tree rings has long been the field of the specialist. Those who have taken it up have done so with some particular scientific background and objective and there has been a general impression that understanding of the principles involved calls for long, preparatory study.

In many other sciences, however, it has been demonstrated that popularization is not only possible but highly desirable. For example, a Boy Scout's chemistry set of today can make demonstrations (and prove a knowledge of fundamentals) which would have astounded leading chemists of an earlier day. So with study of tree rings, there is no reason why it should not be open to the amateur. In short, it could offer all who love the forest trees a new route to adventure in exploratory science. There is really nothing mysterious or beyond comprehension about tree-ring analysis; it can well become a hobby in which intriguing discoveries could be made almost from the start.

It has only remained for someone with the necessary inclination and talent to provide in popular form an attractive and reliable introduction to this new field.

Earlier printings of this useful book have clarified and con-

* Dr. Glock has been an authority on tree-ring analysis for some 30 years, presently heads the Laboratory for Tree-Ring Research at Macalester College, Saint Paul, Minn. He is the author of numerous publications on this subject prepared for the Carnegie Institution of Washington and the Smithsonian Institution and is also conducting a comprehensive study of tree growth in relation to climate for the National Science Foundation.

densed identification of the conifer species for thousands who wanted to recognize and to know the native trees but had neither time nor inclination to labor with botanical reference works. Thus, Doctor Bowers' book filled a real need by making available the author's simple, systematic methods for identifying conifers native to the Pacific Coast. Later he again pioneered the way for beginners by providing another short cut—with no prerequisite of long or scientific preparation—and encouraging them to study and apply the principles of tree-ring analysis.

It has been my good fortune to work with Doctor Bowers in the forests as well as in his laboratory. On numerous trips into the far places of the high Sierra it has been a privilege to have his company and to come to know him as a scientist who brings to his study of trees the training and experience of a long and successful career as a civil engineer. In recent years he has made real contributions to the science of dendrochronology. Now that he turns his ability of expression to popularizing that science, it is a pleasure to give the new fifth printing a cordial welcome to our literature on tree-ring analysis.

WALDO S. GLOCK

Saint Paul, Minnesota
March 1956

FOREWORD TO THE SEVENTH PRINTING

By W. G. McGinnies *

New material in this printing incorporates the results of three years of a continuing study on bristlecone pines being carried on at The Laboratory of Tree-Ring Research, The University of Arizona, Tucson, Arizona. The chronology-building phase of this research, begun by the late Edmund Schulman, has been continued by Dr. C. W. Ferguson, who had been his assistant during the initial study. The present project, aided by two grants from the National Science Foundation, has confirmed Dr. Schulman's finding that individual specimens of bristlecone pine reach ages of over 4,600 years. This assurance of an age that exceeds by 1,400 years that of the giant sequoia, long thought to be the oldest living thing, has focused unprecedented attention on the relatively little-known bristlecone pine.

The long and exacting study of this species has applied principles of tree-ring analysis to measurement and comparison of many thousands of growth rings to establish the longest chronology thus far developed. The data now being transferred to electronic computer cards provides a basis for analysis that will open up avenues for future studies on the climate of the past, far exceeding the most optimistic hopes of A. E. Douglass, the founder of the modern science of dendrochronology.

---

* Dr. McGinnies has been, for four years, Director of the Laboratory of Tree-Ring Research, The University of Arizona, Tucson, Arizona, the largest and most active laboratory of its kind in the world. Under his directorship extensive studies have been carried on by the several departments of the Laboratory for various national organizations and the United States government. One of these, presently in its third year of financing by the National Science Foundation, is the comprehensive analysis of bristlecone pine data on which a summary of findings to date makes its first appearance in the seventh printing of Cone-Bearing Trees of the Pacific Coast.

In this same three-year period there have been several advances in techniques at the Laboratory of Tree-Ring Research resulting from contributions made by Dr. Nathan A. Bowers, a Research Associate in Dendrochronology. He has developed core-taking tools of original design, one of which was granted a U.S. patent in 1963. A notable advance in laboratory practice has followed the development, under Dr. Bowers' direction, of an entirely new concept in surfacing wood specimens for microscopic study by using a sanding machine of novel design, weighing three quarters of a ton, which employs the principle of abrasive cutting along a line rather than simultaneous abrasion over an area having both length and breadth.

In addition to the work on bristlecone pine, presently under way at the Laboratory by a staff of scientists and their assistants (the total staff varies from twenty to twenty five or more), are studies on what can be learned from other tree species about long-range climatic changes and the dating of prehistoric ruins, including the dating of over 10,000 wood and charcoal samples from archaeological sites in the United States, Mexico, and the Near East. The present collections are the largest in the world. They contain some 100,000 prehistoric tree-ring specimens and about 25,000 cores and sections taken from living trees or trees which have died recently.

Current emphasis is on modern codification of ring data, better understanding of growth problems, extension of ring chronologies into the past, the discovery of new datable species, and the expansion of tree-ring dating techniques into new areas of the world.

W. G. McGinnies

Tucson, Arizona
October 31, 1964

An Introduction to Tree-Ring Analysis

You who enjoy the beauty of Pacific Coast forests and have spent happy hours in them, learning to recognize and to know our native conifers, may find a new field for adventure in another phase of this same interest, this time looking beneath the surface or inside the bark of our forest trees.

A laboratory with its scientific apparatus is not at all essential to your study of growth rings in trees. All you really need is some general knowledge of the basic principles underlying tree-growth habits, plus the desire to apply this knowledge in a study of whatever tree sections come conveniently to hand—a limb blown off by the wind, a stump where a tree was cut down, or the end of a piece of lumber; these all give an opportunity to examine closely a cross section of wood. And in any cross section you will find a key to the history and characteristics of the growth represented. Such an examination, even though based on only brief study of the subject of tree-ring analysis, will afford a real thrill when you find that you can read and interpret much of what the growth rings so faithfully record.

Native conifers on the Pacific Coast—unlike some trees in the tropics—record their growth in a manner now well understood by specialists who have made long-time studies of them. You can quickly learn some of the fundamentals and then use this knowledge as you explore and study further on your own account. You may be surprised and sometimes amazed by what you will discover.

If we start by closely examining any one of our native conifers, we shall see how and why it lays down so accurate a record of when and how much it grew. The annual growth record is made throughout the entire framework of the tree—that is, in the limbs as well as in the trunk itself. On the Pacific Coast the climate favors a growing season and a dormant season. In the spring, when the days lengthen and the warm sun coaxes out new foliage, the whole tree stirs with nature's irresistible demand for growth. As the foliage increases the area spread out to absorb the sun's rays, the roots reach down into soil soaked by winter rains, obtain there the necessary life-giving liquid and send it surging upward through tube-like cells, now forming rapidly to aid in this function, between last season's growth and the inner surface of the bark. This upward surge of sap occurs only in this one zone, that is, in outer rings of the sapwood and in new cells forming next to the bark. These cells, when the spring growth period arrives, increase in number, rapidly expand, and prepare to handle the surge of sap circulation that is a vital part of the growth process.

This increase and growth of the tube-like cells may continue until the total width of newly formed material has thickened to as much as a quarter or perhaps a half inch. Then, as the summer passes and the tree completes its seasonal growth, the demand for sap subsides (or the supply of available moisture is exhausted) and cell growth decreases. As sap flow lessens, newly formed cells are smaller and are crowded more closely together. In this compact form they present a generally darker color and a firmer texture. The dormant period thus is preceded by the dark, densewood layer which is that part of each year's growth most easily distinguished when counting off the successive growth rings. The densewood, consisting of these small, dark and closely crowded cells, usually terminates in a sharply defined line formed by the notable contrast between the small cells of densewood immediately preceding the dormant season, and the large, thin-walled cells formed by the first surge of spring growth. It is this line which you will soon learn to recognize as marking the termination of one growth cycle and the beginning of another.

Examine the end of any piece of pine or redwood timber and you will see that in successive growth rings the large cells of spring growth make up the relatively light colored, soft portions of the wood; the small, closely crowded cells make a dark ring representing the slower growth which precedes the dormant period. Thickness of the rings vary, sometimes from very thick to very thin. This is the point at which you may feel a quickening of interest.

You may learn, for example, that in a garden favored with rich soil and ample moisture, a young Monterey pine will show annual radial growth as much as three-quarters of an inch in thickness. That is, the diameter of the tree may increase by 1½ inches in one year. If this continues for a ten-year period the tree will have attained a diameter of 15 inches. Now contrast this with the section of a limb from one of the high-altitude junipers (J-3 in the manual) which you may bring home from a vacation trip to the high Sierra. After cutting a cross section from such a limb and polishing it, inspection with a magnifying glass may disclose a surprisingly close ring spacing, with perhaps more than 200 rings in a single inch. In other words, you will find wide range in growth rates: a single ring in some varieties may be ¾ inch thick or it may occupy less than one two hundredth part of an inch in slower growing species.

In conifers it is normal for the age of a branch to be about the same as that of the trunk at the level of emergence. This results from the natural growth habit of these trees in putting out branches at the tree top in proportion to the rate of progress of the leader or topmost growth. However, since branch diameter is much less than that of the trunk, the rings are crowded more closely together in a branch than in the trunk. In a test made by Doctor Glock to explore this relationship, a tree 19 feet high was felled and sectioned so as to cut across both trunk and limb at the point of emergence. The trunk radius was 3 inches and that of the branch ½ inch, that is, the ratio of average ring thickness, trunk to limb, was six to one.

Rules To Remember

Tree growth may be a complex process in some aspects, but it follows certain fundamental patterns you can readily understand when you have mastered a few simple rules. The first rule to remember is that as successive seasons roll around and each new cycle is started, the tree merely adds something outside what was there before—it puts on a new dress. In the trunk, in the limbs, and in the roots it puts on this new growth right over what was there before. More particularly, the addition is a new ring of wood laid next to and on the outer surface of what was added in the previous season's growth.

Don't confuse yourself by trying to apply this growth rule to

Fig. 1

Fig. 1. *Bottom.* Enlarged photographs of growth rings from two trees. In each ring the light portion is the large-celled growth of spring; the dark portion is the denser growth; i.e., the smaller cells formed prior to dormancy. Note the sharply defined line that marks completion of each growth cycle. That these two specimens grew in the same years is shown by corresponding ring traits. Points of similarity are joined by lines between the two specimens.

Upper right. A plotted record of relative thinness and the specimen from which it was made. This is called a skeleton plot.

Upper left. Two plotted records, placed together for comparison, showing relative degrees of thinness in rings of two trees. Note that such close conformity (more than 80 per cent) betokens the same causes affecting both trees, i.e., these records match and crossdating has been established.

foliage—there it does not apply. Foliage, to be sure, comes out in a new dress each season, but each year it drops off most of the previous season's growth. This is not the same plan followed by the wood itself. In the wood proper, that is, under the bark on limb, trunk, and root, nothing is dropped off or wasted. Instead, all growth is left in place, year after year, to increase the size and provide the constantly increasing structural strength needed to form and support the tree as a whole. This, indeed, is how a tree "makes wood."

The second rule to keep in mind is that in trunk, limbs, and roots, new wood growth occurs only on the *outer surfaces* of the wood. That is, not outside the bark but just under it. Most of the bark itself (certainly the outer portions) is merely a wrapping or protective covering to shield nature's processes which are taking place in delicate operations beneath the surface. Thus the bark is not part of the wood but serves as protection for the sensitive surface of the growing wood. And this growth in the wood takes place just under the bark.

It is in this area, including the sapwood and inner bark, that the life blood (sap) of the tree circulates. Each year a new layer of wood is put on and then, at the end of the growing season, whatever wood growth was made is sealed off, as it were, to remain just exactly that way so long as the tree lives. This is what makes tree-ring analysis so fascinating because nature's process leaves a faithful, historical record of just what happened to the tree and what it did in rate and time of growth, in each successive season throughout its entire life.

The important thing to know here is that the growth near the inner part of the bark is the *youthful* part of the tree. Each year its enthusiasm is renewed in due season and, in accord with the degree to which the tree enjoys conditions favorable to growth, there will be development and expansion in the form of a new layer of wood cells. The layer added each season will be thicker or thinner in accord with growing conditions.

This vital, living part of the tree is called the cambium or the cambium layer, which is a living tissue with most remarkable properties. Its cells on the outer face subdivide to form bark and on the inner face the daughter cells form wood. The zone close to this most vital part of the tree, that is, in the adjoining wood layers, known as sapwood, and in the inner portion of the bark, is the only part of trunk, branch or root where growth can be manifest. It is here and here only that the additional wood layers are added each year.

Also in this zone, and here only, is the curious two-way exchange or circulatory system which carries moisture up from the roots and food down from the foliage. In the springtime, roots extract moisture and dissolved minerals from the soil and send them up to the foliage where sunlight, through a process called photosynthesis, manufactures the food materials on which the tree lives and grows. These food products must be distributed and this is done through the live, active cells recently formed along the inner side of the bark. This distribution of food, mostly downward, constitutes the second half of the two-way exchange.

Proof of the importance of this growth-zone lies in the fact that trees can be killed by "girdling"—that is, by making a cut, with knife or axe, entirely around the tree, through bark and the adjoining wood, to break the continuity in this circulatory system.

This "living layer" close to the inner part of the bark surrounds all parts of the tree from the deepest root to the topmost twig. It may help to think of the trunk of a large tree as being made up of five parts, namely, (1) the inner core of inactive heartwood, (2) the living sapwood, (3) the cambium layer, (4) the inner, living layer of bark, and (5) the inert or dead outer bark.

Preparing Specimens for Ring Counts

A freshly-cut cross section of a tree, such as a stump left after the tree has been felled, offers an attractive place to begin counting rings because here you have a tree definitely dated by its cutting. The ring just inside the bark, of course, is the ring of the most recent growing season; starting there, you can count inward to determine the year when the tree made its first growth ring at this height. Many of our native conifers require little or no preparation of the surface to make the rings legible in a freshly cut cross section. Even a well-weathered stump of a redwood may be still quite readable, since the early, light, wood cells, when exposed, weather more quickly than do the harder, darker dense wood rings, and the resultant ridges often can be counted readily.

For dead wood having less favorable types of wood fiber and for some trees which show little difference between fast- and slow-

Fig. 2

Fig. 2. Starting with a growth-ring of known date, such as the outer ring on a stump (A), and by crossdating from near the center to rings near the outer portion of a second specimen (as in B) there is then available a series of growth rings in B for finding agreement with a third specimen, and so on. By using beams from cliff dwellings and other wood preserved a long time, sequences have thus been continued for many centuries.

growing portions of the rings, you may have to cut across the specimen with a fine-toothed saw and then smooth the surface with sandpaper or a power-sander to make the successive rings stand out. If this proves difficult work, select the most favorable route from center to bark and polish only a narrow path along this line on which to examine successive rings. Where the rings are very close, as in slow-growing trees, a magnifying glass will help you make an accurate count and a needle point will be convenient for marking five- or ten-ring points.

The U.S. Forest Service and some lumber companies find extensive use for an instrument known as an "increment core borer" or the Pressler corer, which is made in Sweden. This instrument (cost about $35) is satisfactory for use in soft woods, to take cores of about 3/16-inch diameter up to a maximum length of 15 inches. It is too short to have wide application on our larger trees and even for these short cores it is not recommended for use on oaks, junipers, or other very dense woods.

Cores taken by this tool (if the rings are not easily readable on the untreated wood) may be glued to a grooved plywood strip and then treated so as to make the individual rings stand out. Treatment may be by sanding and then polishing in the same way that other cross section cuts are made to present more readable surfaces.

The removal of these cores does not harm the trees if the boring is made at a time of year when the sap flow can quickly heal the wound and seal off the hole at the surface. Recommended treatment is to leave the hole for nature to close except in old, slow-growing trees where grafting wax may be used as a plug.

Rates of Growth To Be Expected

A common error of the beginner, in examining a tree-ring specimen, is to assume that the wide rings necessarily mean wet years. This is true only for a location where the amount of moisture available to the tree is the determining factor that controls rate of growth. More often than not there are other factors that exert as much or more influence on the tree's growth than does rainfall. For example, some authorities point out that in *Sequoia gigantea*, narrow rings are more likely to indicate cool summers or short growing seasons. Sunshine, drainage, wind, and the length of the growing season are only a few of the growth factors. Damage to the crown of the tree may result in several to many thin rings.

A fine redwood section given to the author by Professor Emanuel Fritz shows close, very thin rings for a large part of its life span and then a sudden change to thick rings which were formed in every one of the remaining years. This does not mean that the rains came late in the life of this tree and were constant thereafter. Explanation, rather, lies in the fact that at the point of change some adjacent trees were cut down; thereafter sunlight streamed in to increase greatly a rate of growth previously hampered by shade. Such an increase in growth rate is an expected result of thinning out dense forest stands.

Redwood railroad ties with fewer than eight growth rings per inch have been rejected, under specifications used for a long time by the Southern Pacific Railroad, because they would be too soft for suitable service in the track. On the other hand, redwood ring counts ranging up to 60 or 80 per inch are not unknown. An average of a considerable number of redwood ring counts gave the figure of 20 rings per inch. This is an unsafe figure to apply to any particular tree, of course, but it does serve as a convenient rule of thumb by which to compare relative rates of growth.

The rate of growth in *Sequoia gigantea* does not seem to differ widely from its close relative the *Sequoia sempervirens*. Young trees of both species grow very rapidly under favorable conditions and a comparison of some notable ring counts in older trees shows marked similarity. For example, a *gigantea* 22 feet in diameter felled in Sequoia National Park a few years ago had 2,222 rings— an average of about 17 rings per inch. Other examples in both species range both sides of the 20-per-inch rough figure.

How Tree Diameters Can Be Misleading

The surprising facts revealed by tree-ring analysis make it clear that one can go far astray by using the relative diameters of two trees as a measure of their relative ages, even when the trees are of the same species and growing in the same soil. For example, two redwoods, set out side by side by the author some fourteen years ago, when both had diameters comparable to a lead pencil, came from the same parent tree and had exactly the same care and soil in which to grow. One has now developed into a fine tree

Fig. 3

Fig. 3. This oak (*Quercus agrifolia*), on the Stanford University campus, had a diameter of 8 feet and was thought to be very old. However, when felled and sectioned the "trunk" was found to be a hollow cylinder composed of five separate trees. Probably starting as a "clump" of saplings, the separate trunks grew, overlapped and were pressed together as a more or less circular shell in which there never was a single, common center. Although only five separate centers of growth survived, there may have been more at the outset. By counting rings in one of the first-order branches, cut 19 feet above the ground, and adding an allowance for growth to the 19-foot height, the age of this curious tree was finally rated at not more than 175 years. (Photo by Gene Tupper) more than 15 inches in diameter at one foot above ground; the other measures a scant 4 inches. No one would guess they are the same age, yet core borings from both would show that they have the same number of rings.

It should be remembered, too, that some trees have a "dwarf tendency" even under good growing conditions. Of two ponderosa pine trees taken from the same lot of seed by the Institute of Forest Genetics, planted side by side and given the same treatment for 20 years, one was 20 feet tall and the other 1 foot.

The danger of reaching false conclusions based on relative diameters is brought out convincingly by the botanist Willis L. Jepson ("Silva of California," page 58) in a tabulation of data from ring counts he made on the stumps of Sequoia gigantea in the Converse Basin. Some examples from his tabulation are as follows:

Tree Number	Diameter	Age
8	11 ft. 7 in. @ 12 ft.	2,017
9	11 ft. 10 in. @ 7 ft.	940
12	15 ft. 4 in. @ 10 ft.	2,177
16	24 ft. 2 in. @ 5 ft.	1,346

We must not be misled into using relative diameters of trees, even of the same species and in the same general area, as any indication of their ages. "Estimates" of age can also be quite misleading. Jepson cites an example of this in an unwise attempt to apply an "average" of 20 rings per inch in estimating the age of a Big Tree: when the "Father of the Forest" was to be cut down, estimates of its age, applying the 20-ring per inch figure, indicated that its diameter of 27 feet inside the bark, should show an age of some 3,240 years. But when an actual ring count on the stump was made it was found that the age was only about 1,300 years (about 8 rings per inch average.)

The well-known tendency of promotion groups to exaggerate tree ages can be at once a challenge and an opportunity for the tree-ring hobbyist. ("Older than the Egyptian pyramids" was the claim made in a recent case.) With these exaggerations in mind, a few examples of authentic ring counts on native trees of the West Coast should be useful.

The oldest Sequoia sempervirens on which there is a record of authentic ring count was about 2,300 years old. The maximum count for the *Sequoia gigantea* is upward of 3,000 and will be discussed in more detail later. California oak trees, on the other hand are rarely as old as boosters have claimed. Few are believed, by some authorities, to live much more than 300 years. An example is "El Roble Grande," the big oak of Lake County, California (9 feet 3 inches in diameter) which was long thought to have great age. After it blew down in a 1952 storm, a ring count showed its age to be about 335 years.

Another large oak (*Quercus agrifolia*) cut down on the Stanford campus (1954) interested the author because its 8-foot diameter and the fact that there would be access to the full cross section for ring counts, suggested an opportunity to get authentic data on a large, old oak. This tree (Fig. 3) had no branches up to a height of some 18 feet and the trunk seemed to be a fine, healthy specimen. When it was felled, however, the "trunk" was found to be a shell composed of five separate trunks, each with its independent ring center. There was not then, and in all probability never had been any central growth in the center of this shell. Explanation probably lies in its starting from a thicket of young trees close together, all of about the same age. From the thicket, five stems or trunks could grow up to form a ring (perhaps choking out others) and as progressive growth pressed the several individuals together, one growth zone overlapped another until there was what appeared, outwardly, to be only a single trunk. In numerous places on this anomalous growth, wood and bark formed on the outside of and completely covered wood and bark of another entirely separate "tree."

A still more striking example of this phenomenon of multiple trunk growths, according to some authorities, obtains in a tree (*Taxodium mucronatum*) near Oaxaca, Mexico, which is said to be perhaps the most famous tree in all Mexico (Fig. 4). It is known as "El Tule del Santa Maria" and was advertised as having been "estimated by eminent authorities to be 10,000 years old." The basis for any such estimate, of course, has been trunk dimensions, and the size is admittedly impressive. The perimeter of the somewhat elliptical base, one meter above ground, is 116 feet and the major axis of the ellipse is about 40 feet. H. A. Dutton, who has examined this tree repeatedly, rates it as a multiple-trunk growth, probably about 500 years old.

In California, tourists on the Monterey Peninsula have been told that the gnarled and twisted Monterey cypresses are "thousands of years old." But a study of these trees by a dendrologist rated the oldest of them as not more than 350 years. Mr. Dutton believes their maximum age is considerably less.

Our forest trees do have great age and such interesting histories that it is quite unnecessary to exaggerate. A study of growth rings enables one to read from the record the tree itself has made, much that was only mystery before. Moreover, the ring counts can provide proof in the matter of age.

Oak trees often separate, only a few feet above ground, into several trunks or first-order branches (not to be confused with "limbs"). Yet the estimates of age in such trees usually is based on the size of the trunk at ground level. Tree-ring analysis provides a means of checking such estimates with ring counts on first-order branches just above the fork. It is possible that a rule should be established to the effect that "The age of an oak whose trunk quickly divided into first-order branches of near-equal size, may be estimated by making a ring count close to the fork in one of these branches and adding thereto adequate allowance for the time it probably took this particular tree to grow to the height at which the primary-branch ring count was made."

False Rings and Multiple Rings

In your exploration of tree rings you must not expect to find them always the same; nature likes to vary growth to suit innumerable changes in conditions—sometimes it is not even apparent that conditions are different. Professor Emanuel Fritz, a well-known authority on the growth of redwoods, has reported on ring counts in that species with as much as 20 per cent more rings on one part of the perimeter than elsewhere. This condition is not common, of course, but is indicative of what you may discover on occasion if you explore tree-ring analysis far enough.

A more common deviation from the uniform ring pattern is the tendency of rings to crowd together in some portion of their perimeter, so that for some distance two or more rings appear to be only one. You can discover this to best advantage if you follow along each ring for as much of the perimeter as possible— if it seems to combine with another ring, it may separate again farther on.

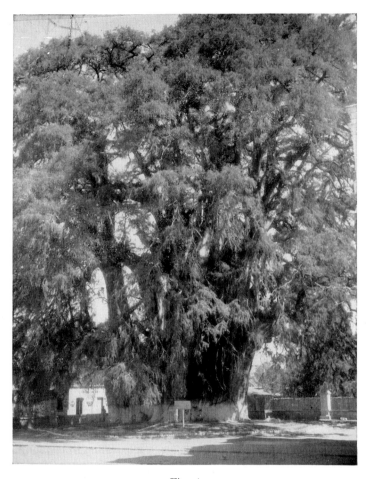

Fig. 4

Fig. 4. This tree, "El Tule del Santa Maria," near Oaxaca, Mexico, has in one direction a base thickness of 40 feet. (For scale, see the man whose outline shows just to the left of the trunk.) It has been advertised as having an age "estimated by eminent authorities as 10,000 years" but this claim is not borne out by proof such as tree-ring analysis makes possible. H. A. Dutton estimated the actual age of this trunk-cluster at about 500 years. (Photo courtesy F. P. Cronemiller)

A quite different deviation from normal is found in intermediate or false rings which sometimes appear along part or all of an otherwise regularly-formed ring. Such a ring indicates a false start in that particular growth period. But such rings are "false" only in the sense that they do not represent a full year's growth. The experienced ring analyst usually can distinguish them by the fact that they lack the sharp line of demarcation characteristic of the true annual ring. The well-defined line normally marks the outer edge of last growth preceding the dormant period and which is followed by the larger cells of the next spring season.

There are a few trees which put on multiple rings each year. Examine a section from your pepper tree (*Schinus molle,* a native of South America but grown on our West Coast for decorative purposes) and you will find that it may put on a new growth ring as often as ten or fifteen times in one year.

Crossdating Tree Rings As a Hobby

Crossdating (or cross-identification) is the establishing of time identity between ring groups in different trees. In other words, if a group of rings somewhere near the center of a young tree (A) in Fig. 2 can be shown to have been formed in the same years as rings near the bark of an older tree (B) then a continuous year count can be made through the sum total of non-overlapping rings in the two trees. By using a succession of trees in this manner, it has been possible to extend the year-by-year count of rings back for centuries. This has great value in climatic studies and in establishing the age of ancient wood samples and, by inference, the age of the earth formation or historic structures in which they were found.

The process of crossdating, whose discovery in 1911 is ascribed to A. E. Douglass, deals with the *relative,* not the *absolute,* thickness of tree rings. And it is abnormality in thinness, not thickness, to which observation should be particularly directed. This is because, in the arid areas where crossdating is most successful, absence of rainfall is the condition which has the most marked effect on the amount of annual growth. Hence if the degree or severity of the drought can be indicated in a proportional manner, this then becomes the critical feature on which comparisons can be made between rings in different trees.

Let us adopt a basis for rating thinness as (1) thin, (2) very thin, and (3) extremely thin. Now if, in the rings of different trees, extreme thinness occurs in some corresponding way (two or three together, or with some corresponding interval) this will readily become apparent when the records are compared. When, by this method, drought peculiarities in one tree can be shown to agree by 80 per cent with the same characteristics in another tree, the two ring series are said to be "matched" and crossdating has been established.

A common way to make these comparisons is to plot on a piece of cross section paper a series of lines whose lengths represent the relative thinness of the growth rings. Each horizontal space on the paper represents one year (or one growth ring); no lines are plotted for the average rings or the thick rings, but the thin, the very thin, and the extremely thin rings, on the other hand, are plotted as lines whose lengths vary in proportion the degree of thinness. These skeleton plots can then be moved slowly past one another to see if they match. If and when they do, crossdating has been established.

An example of how such plots appear is shown in Fig. 1. Here two such plots are placed side by side for comparison and it is seen that definite crossdating has been established, beyond a doubt, by agreement of more than 80 per cent of the characteristics—persuasive evidence that the same causes were operative in both cases.

How this principal of crossdating is made to bridge the centuries is shown by the diagram in Fig. 2. Dr. Douglass, who worked with charred wood left in fireplaces used by prehistoric men or with cross sections of beams used in building their homes, was able to date construction of the prehistoric cliff-dwellings of the Southwest. One of these, Dr. Douglass writes, was built in 919 A.D., others in the 1060's and still others at later dates.

Along most of the Pacific Coast, west of the Sierra, crossdating is difficult; but in the dry regions east of the mountains and in Arizona, Nevada, Utah, and parts of Colorado, it is relatively simple because in these comparatively arid regions rainfall becomes a determining factor in the amount of annual growth. Severe drought, particularly for several successive years, shows an effect on tree growth more markedly than is likely to result from any one variable in regions of more plentiful rainfall.

And at this point, because the subject affords a great deal of fun for anyone who may care to pursue it as a hobby, the following references on crossdating are included:

Principles and Methods of Tree-Ring Analysis, by W. S. Glock, Carnegie Institution of Washington, Publication No. 486 (1937).

Tree-Ring Analysis on the Douglass System, by W. S. Glock, *Pan-American Geologist*, XL (1933), 1–14.

Dating Prehistoric Ruins by Tree-Rings, by W. S. Stallings, Jr., Lab. Anthro., Gen. Ser., *Bull.*, VIII (1939), 1–20 (Sante Fe, N. M.).

Dating Pueblo Bonito and Other Ruins of the Southwest, by A. E. Douglass. Nat. Geog. Soc., Contributed technical paper, Pueblo Bonito Series, No. 1 (1935), p. 43.

What Are The "Oldest Living Things?"

Since tree-ring analysis has advanced so much in recent years, there is now some prospect that previous unsupported estimates of age may give way to proof provided by actual ring counts. This may again bring up the question as to whether *Sequoia gigantea,* so long hailed as "the oldest living things" are really the oldest. The high altitude junipers (J-3 in the manual) have been suggested as possible candidates for this honor. Though not outstanding in the matter of size, these grand old trees are deserving of much more attention than they have received.

Ring counts in the junipers, so far as it has been possible to make them, have shown extremely slow growth rates. Mr. C. K. Bennett (quoted on page 81 of the manual) reports ring counts as high as 400 per inch on one limb section. But the juniper wood is so hard that it is difficult to take cores with boring tools not specially designed for this work. It is hoped that when a power corer is available it will provide proof of the very great age of these old trees, as it also should make possible definite age-dating of the *Sequoia gigantea.*

This latter point (maximum age of a Big Tree) is a moot question when we come down to actual, verified ring counts as distinct from "estimates." For a long time the figure of 3,126 was accepted as the maximum authentic record of ring counts on the Big Trees. (This figure is given by Frye and White in their book "The Big Trees," page 35.) However, there are still higher figures which should be considered in any final test of the "oldest living thing." Perhaps the most intriguing of the greater-age figures is that recorded by no less an authority than John Muir himself.

On page 182 of his book, "The Mountains of California" (now long out of print), he described the trunk of a fallen Big Tree which had been burned half through. He says, "I spent a day in estimating its age, clearing away the charred surface with an axe and carefully counting the annual rings with the aid of a pocket lens. The wood rings in the section I laid bare were so involved and so contorted in some places that I was not able to determine its age exactly, but I counted over 4,000 rings."

Because this figure is larger than any other record of actual ring counts, Muir's statement was referred by the author to H. A. Dutton (Stanford graduate in botany, class of 1900) with inquiry as to whether the figure had ever been verified. Selecting Dutton for reference was a happy choice, since he had himself, years ago, tried hard to verify this same count. He reported that soon after graduation from Stanford he called on Muir and discussed this ring count with him. Muir drew a map to show just where the trunk could be found.

Dutton made two trips into the area to which Muir directed him but despite diligent search for several days he was unable to locate the trunk described. However, as Dutton observed, fires in the mountains were very common in those early days. "Sheep men burned off the brush to let the grass grow, hunters set fires in the canyons to drive out the game and campers were careless." These are indeed plausible explanations as to the disappearance of the tree which Dutton's expeditions were unable to locate. His written report on this (in the author's possession) is that "Muir almost surely miscounted. How could he have *counted* the rings? He does not say he sawed the log in two."

Other questions, other quests are bound to be made. One of the projects in the author's laboratory at the present time is the design and construction of a power-driven corer for taking cores on the order of a half-inch in diameter (a) from hardwood trees and (b) from soft wood trees, in lengths sufficient to reach to the central point in the larger *Sequoia gigantea*. What will ring counts disclose on cores taken by boring to the central point of a tree 33 feet in diameter? Quests of this sort intrigue and offer reward to those who make a study of tree-ring analysis.

LIFE AT A PRICE

A native of the "High Places," silently
eloquent of centuries in wind and ice

Inspirational Trees

The trees pictured and described on the following fifteen pages illustrate difficulties that often must be surmounted for existence in certain locations. Indeed, the basis of selection of these photographs from a great many offered was their thought-provoking quality.

These trees inspire confidence and faith in overcoming obstacles to continued growth and existence. The accompanying texts—perhaps they could be called "sermonettes"—are presented to the reader in a way intended to stimulate his thinking and thus enhance his enjoyment of our forests on his trips to the "High Places."

Battling the Elements

These two pictures of a White-bark Pine (*P. albicaulis*), one "downwind" and one "crosswind," present eloquent evidence of a centuries-long battle with the elements. Comparison of the "crosswind" view with page xxxvi of this volume brings together pictures of this same tree made 22 years apart (1934, 1956). The later view, opposite, shows a tree still strong and healthy; lush growth at the base proves that it has learned to hug the rocks for protection, and even the branches that cling to the lee side of the trunk are green and alive all the way up, albeit the extent of their growth diminishes with the height, indicating the lessening shelter as the trunk diameter narrows.

Its location on a rocky ridge at an elevation of 8,000′, with no shelter from terrific winter gales and where food is always in short supply, causes one to marvel that the tree should survive at all; that it has lived all this time is an inspiring example of perseverance. To stand before this tree and study the mute evidence it offers is to regard it with reverence, a feeling that deepens as one envisions the intensity of winter's sleet-laden blasts, battering a living thing for centuries in such an exposed spot. One leaves its presence lifted up by a stimulating, inspirational experience, perhaps with a resolve to face life's difficulties so bravely as to earn, in old age, a "well done."

(Location: Summit of ridge northwest of Mt. Rubicon, west side of Lake Tahoe. Photo by author.)

The Gargoyle Tree

This large Redwood, bent over almost at right angles not far above its base, is a curiosity about which there has been much speculation. Here is a tree belying the rule about Redwoods having straight trunks. Since it would be impossible to *bend* a trunk with the 14-foot diameter this tree has, such an anomaly must exemplify the old rule that "as the twig is bent, so the tree will grow." This is the point at which speculation begins—details were published in *Trees* magazine for November-December 1957.

This tree warrants analytical study because of the indications to be found supporting the theory about early bending. One of the most significant clues is that stubs of a branchlike nature, protruding from the apex of the bend, were found by a Stanford University cytologist to be roots, not branches. This at once suggests earth at this level and recalls the botanical rule that moist earth in contact with the bark of a Redwood invites formation of roots. That the tree could and did grow this way gives rise to wonder and respect for an undaunted endeavor to continue its growth under such abnormal conditions. This tree is a study that rewards inspection and thoughtful contemplation.

(Location: On Old Woman Creek (branch of Gazos) about 3 miles inland and 2 miles south of Pigeon Point Lighthouse, San Mateo Co., Calif. Willis photo, copyrighted.)

The Oldest Known Living Things

Bristlecone pines (*P. aristata*) grow in scattered locations in six southwestern states, but very special attention attaches to those found in the White Moutains of Southeastern California, near the boundary between that state and Nevada. There, it has been discovered, they have overcome extremely difficult living conditions to attain an age greater than any other living thing so far as known, anywhere in the world. Why this great age could be attained here and only here, where living conditions are so adverse has intrigued those who do research in this field. But apart from technical considerations, the inspirational angle has universal appeal. To see and admire these old patriarchs in their native habitat is to feel very close to the mysteries of nature.

About 1950, Dr. N. T. Mirov of Berkeley, California, assisted by forest ranger A. E. Noren of Big Pine, made exploratory surveys of these trees and drew attention to their great age. R. E. Burton, after visiting them in 1953, wrote that "they live the most austere of lives amidst the most rigorous environment and on the scantiest rations of food and water. Their life is one of constant struggle against the elements: only the fit survive."

From 1953 to 1957, Dr. Edmund Schulman took core borings and made many ring counts on the *P. aristata* which prove that they attain an age exceeding 4,600 years, or 1,400 years more than the maximum verified ring count on the *S. gigantea*. The United States Forest Service has taken steps to preserve the principal stands of these trees by classifying a 28,000-acre portion of the Inyo National Forest as "The Ancient Bristlecone Pine Forest," a botanical area to be managed for scientific study and public enjoyment. Part of this area has been officially named the Edmund Schulman Memorial Grove.

(Location: The White Mountain habitat of these trees, about 17 miles northeast of Big Pine, California, is accessible in summer via a road starting up from Westgard Pass. Photo by R. E. Burton.) For more information see pages liii and 120–121.

Heredity Importance

Heredity is of great importance in selecting trees to be shown as well-formed representatives of a species or as ornamental types for study and comparison. This will be apparent from this picture showing the tops of a grove in which all the trees are *Sequoia sempervirens*. The one on the right comes of a different parentage from the others and only this one has regular branches, symmetrical and shapely in their formation. All the others have a "grotesque" form, with crooked, twisting branches and trunks deformed by leaders that were repeatedly replaced, after they bent out of the vertical so far as to be superseded by one of the upper limbs.

In this grove all but the one on the extreme right are offshoots of a Redwood whose traits and characteristics are the same as those evident in this second-generation growth. Because this grove was set out in its infancy by an observer who knew of the parentage and watched the characteristics develop, the record is complete from the time of planting until the trees were about 80' high.

Selection of parents is all-important where typical traits are wanted in the second generation.

(Location: Tree tops of a Redwood grove planted in 1941 at 184 Tuscaloosa Ave., Atherton, Calif. Photo by author.)

"Los Milenarios"

When reports of very old Olive trees came from the Spanish island of Majorca (in the Mediterranean) to a dendrology student in this country, a request promptly went back for a cross section, if possible, and trunk measurements d.b.h. (diameter breast high—quoting the usual U. S. Forest Service formula for measurement). The reply from Spain, accompanied by one of these pictures, asked, "Where do you get the d.b.h. measurement on a trunk like this?"

Olives are among the tree species mentioned in oldest historical records and doubtless they do attain great age in some locations. However, there is no known authentication of the "thousands of years" claimed by labels placed on some of these oldsters whose post-card pictures (for sale to tourists) are marked "Los Milenarios."

(Location: On the island of Majorca, Mediterranean Sea. Photos by J. O. Asturias.)

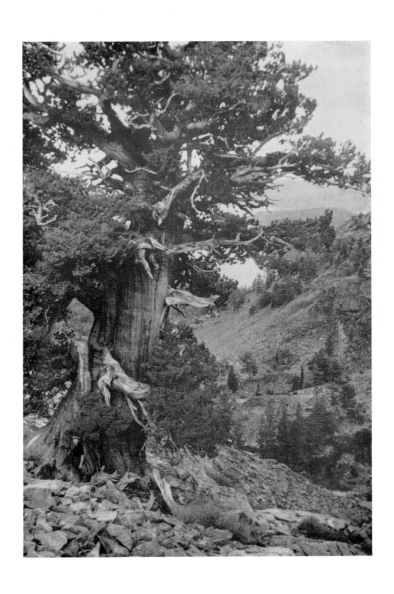

This "Soil" Yields Nutriment?

Junipers of the High Sierra (*Juniperus occidentalis*) often are objects of incredulous comment because they seem to avoid favorable locations in favor of the most inhospitable and even seemingly impossible spots. In "Juniper country" there may be an attractive mountain meadow where soil and moisture abound: but if so, Junipers will not be there. Instead, on some high crag that overlooks that meadow, a Juniper will be found clinging precariously to the most unlikely spot and yet the tree gives evidence that it has lived and thrived there for centuries.

When the tree here shown was young, perhaps two or three thousand years ago, its roots must have found a crevice in the rock containing the necessary minerals and moisture. But now that it has grown to a diameter of some 14' (note the human figure at its base) the only "soil" in sight is the steeply sloping slide of granite blocks. This is not at all unusual for a tree of this interesting species, which offers an opportunity for a study of environmental selection.

This species of Juniper might be likened to those adventurous spirits, the pioneers who built our West. Certainly rigorous existence builds character.

(Location: Southeast of Fallen Leaf Lake, Calif., at an elevation of about 8,200'. Photo by Holbrook Working.)

Trees of the "High Places"

The appearance in summer of this conifer stand crowding the limit known as "timber line," is eloquent of the conditions endured in the age-long march upward in the "High Places." Here the seasons change rapidly from arctic cold in winter to the hot dryness of summer. When the short summer season does afford enough warmth to favor tree growth, roots that force their way into very small crevices in solid granite rocks can find little of the moisture then needed. Thus the trees that survive must develop a storage system suited to this rigorous environment.

This view exemplifies the limiting conditions that control tree growth at the timber line. The bare granite slopes have occasional low spots that retain melted snow (until it evaporates) ; the trees of a species hardy enough for this kind of existence are dwarfed by the adversities of the environment and appear to be even more diminutive by reason of the great gaunt crags that tower above them, formidable, unyielding, and forbidding.

(Location: Timber line on ridge at west end of Kearsarge Pinnacles, looking SSE from west of Bullfrog Lake, Calif. In background, East Vidette, elevation 12,742'. Photo by George Young.)

The great trunk of this Silver Pine (*Pinus monticola*) built up with nourishment secured under difficulties and processed by relatively sparse foliage, is a striking example of a long and thrifty life. Geologists say that glaciers scoured good soil from Sierra "High Places" down to a level lower than that here shown. This tree, then, probably had only a limited supply of minerals and the great trunk is a reminder that wood can be made, by nature, chiefly from air and water through photosynthesis.

(Location: On Tamarack Trail above Fallen Leaf Lake, California, elevation about 7,800′. Photo by Holbrook Working.)

Tree-Ring Studies of
Bristlecone Pines

THE OLDEST KNOWN LIVING THINGS

The science of determining the age of trees by studying the annual growth rings has been progressing steadily through the years. Techniques now in vogue reveal much more and can be applied with much more confidence than was the case a quarter century ago. This is particularly true in the southwestern United States where additions constantly are being made to existing chronologies.

When the first printing of this book appeared in 1942, the commonly accepted belief was that *Sequoia gigantea* could "live to be 5,000 or 10,000 years old or forever, so far as anyone knows" (Frye and White) because no one had ever reported one as having died of old age, but that they were destroyed, rather, by natural causes such as fire, lightning, wind, landslides, etc.

However, these ideas were speculative, and the maximum verified ring count for *Sequoia gigantea* is only about 3,200. As years have passed and greater age for the Sequoias has not been established, the spotlight of attention was focused instead on another species whose recently discovered age has been a surprise to everyone and has deeply intrigued the dendrochronologist.

The bristlecone pine, *Pinus aristata,* has long been known as one of the 17 pines native to the West; but, being of no commercial significance and growing only in scattered stands in high mountain areas of six southwestern states, attracted little attention. But the time came when surprising discoveries were made in the White Mountains of east central California, where bristlecone pines * grow up to timberline at about 11,600′. That the

---

* The chronology aspects of the bristlecone pine study, as of December 1964, were made available for this presentation by the Laboratory of Tree-Ring Research, The University of Arizona, Tucson, Arizona. See color plate frontispiece, also pages 120–121.

species in this area has been found to attain a very great age is attributed to natural conditions unlikely to be duplicated elsewhere, namely, much of the moisture that comes inland from the the Pacific in cloud form is precipitated on the Sierra Nevada, which range in elevation up to 14,000'. Thus the White Mountains, lying to the east of the Sierra and the dry Owens Valley, are in a rain shadow. Despite the fact that bristlecone pines grow at such a high elevation they are here in an arid environment where annual rainfall is only 10" to 15". Also, they are subject to high winds and extremely low temperatures that mean a constant struggle even to maintain life. The significant thing is that under difficult living conditions they have developed a growth form that enables them to outlive any other tree species.

But there is no "amazing secret" to the long life of bristlecone pines. Rather, an understanding of the mechanism by which these trees maintain life in advanced years provides a wholly logical explanation (Schulman and Ferguson, *in* Schulman 1956; Schulman 1958; Wright 1963). It should be said, however, that as the explanation unfolds, one feels a corresponding increase of respect for nature's processes.

The oldest of these trees, it is explained, are found in such an advanced stage of dieback that there may be only a small group of living twigs on one remaining branch. Live wood has decreased in proportion to decrease of life-sustaining nutrients. As the top of the tree dies back, death in the stem keeps pace until relatively few living cells remain. In other words, instead of the whole tree becoming sickly with age, much of the tree gradually dies while the remaining portion not only continues to live but remains quite healthy.

Under the rigors of marginal existence, the needs of the living tissue may exceed the limits of available moisture and soil nutrients. As the trees age, they cannot survive if they are unable to rid themselves of excessive growth. In the oldest specimens, a large part of the tree has been sacrificed by the tree's natural processes in order that the remainder may live.

Another longevity factor is inherent in the quality of the wood itself. Under conditions in the White Mountains, some trees increase as little as ½" in radius per century, and the wood is too highly lignified to support growth of fungi and bacteria that could cause rot. With freedom from decay, wood remains sound to the center of the tree, even long after death and where the center has been exposed by erosion of dead wood.

Unlike other upper timberline species, bristlecone pines in the White Mountains do not take on a dwarfed and distorted appearance (the so-called Krummholz form) near timberline. At the last outpost along their upper elevation limit, they stand erect. Highest elevation range seems to be limited by temperatures during the growing season and not by rigorous winter climate. In other words, young trees simply do not grow in locations where spring and summer temperatures are below their tolerance.

Early survey work on bristlecone pines was done in 1953; but when Schulman reported on them, intensive studies supplied the detailed data needed to prove unprecedented age. In his long-term studies, culminating in the discovery of bristlecone pine as the oldest known living thing, Dr. Schulman combined a knowledge of dendrochronology with wide experience in its application, and to these qualifications he soon added a keen desire to seek out the secrets of age that so long had been concealed in the venerable trunks.

At first, critics questioned the accuracy of a ring count on trees much larger than apparently could be sampled with the standard 18″ increment corer. In circular trunks the short cores might not have been adequate; but a typical instance of coring procedure, as described by Schulman (1958), on the very old trunks is shown in Fig. 5 which is a sketch, to scale, of a horizontal section of a trunk at the level where it was cored. Note that the only part still living is at the extreme upper right of the L-shaped section. In older trees the trunk is very rarely circular in shape; an irregular outline is more typical of bristlecone pines.

To extract a complete core record from the living bark to the inner-most ring, of the section shown in Fig. 5, a core was first taken straight through the bark as far as the boring tool would reach. Then successive cores were taken at angles, as shown, such that each core included some rings also in adjoining cores. This over-lapping made it possible to include the entire ring sequence all the way from the bark to the earliest growth that still remained on the old trunk. This particular section does

23½"

1956 AD

Living wood

Dead wood

Core borer holes

1500 AD

1000 AD

1500

1000

AD

BC

2250 + BC

2000 + BC

1000 + BC

Trunk outline in 2250 BC?

Ring overlap areas crosshatched

41"

· lvi ·

Fig. 5. Sketch, to scale, of horizontal section of a bristlecone pine trunk showing the locations of cores that provided a record of more than 4,000 years. The only portion that still remains alive is the shaded area in the extreme upper right.

not include the earliest rings formed when the tree was young because that portion of the trunk (indicated by dotted lines) has been entirely eroded away.

Schulman's death in 1958 temporarily halted the study of this species, but it was resumed at the Laboratory of Tree-Ring Research in 1961 under directorship of Dr. W. G. McGinnies, with field and laboratory analyses of the chronology-building phase under supervision of Dr. C. W. Ferguson, formerly assistant to Dr. Schulman. During all these years of study and up to December, 1964, work on bristlecone pines of the White Mountains has included sampling more than a thousand trees of which 17 show ages exceeding 4,000 years and one more than 4,600 years. Thus there is little doubt that the bristlecone pines are at least 1,400 years older than the oldest verified ring count on giant Sequoia.

The purpose of the chronology phase of the study has been to establish a tree-ring record of high quality and maximum length for bristlecone pine in the White Mountain area. The greater the number of specimens, of course, the more confidence can be placed in the chronology. Work has been aided by computer programs which have been established for processing dated and measured ring series and by the use of radiocarbon analysis. With these aids and by incorporating records from totally dead trees, it may be that work now under way will extend the chronology far beyond that possible if only living trees were used.

To supplement the chronology building, a comprehensive climatic interpretation has been carried on by Dr. H. C. Fritts, the Laboratory's dendrophysiologist. In his highly instrumented study, in progress for three years as this was written, all phases of environment and tree growth are measured and analyzed. The growth of the trees has been recorded by increment borings, cambial plugs, and observation of stem elongation and cone development; measurements have been made by six dendrographs and 20 dendrometers. With the established chronologies in other areas of the Southwest for comparison, it has been possible to show that there is a statistically valid correlation of the bristlecone pine records with those of other species and areas for distances as much as 1,000 miles to the east and some 300 miles to the southeast.

Apart from this scientific progress, it is interesting to note how accessibility of the "Ancient Bristlecone Pine Forest" has changed as interest in the trees has increased. When A. E. Noren, then U.S. Forest Service Ranger at Bishop, California, reported on the bristlecone pines about 1950, their locale was well-nigh inaccessible—their steep and rugged terrain was so remote and travel was so difficult that only a few hardy and really interested men got to see them. But the trees were most intriguing, and the reports that each visitor helped to spread brought other visitors. R. E. Burton and Woodbridge Metcalf made repeated pilgrimages because, like others, they loved the thought-stimulating grandeur of the ancient trunks. As more and more visitors came, the trails that pack animals used became jeep routes and then a road "for four-wheel-drive vehicles only." By the summer of 1964 there was a good road, with not unreasonable grades, that was paved almost all the way to the 10,000′ level at Edmund Schulman Memorial Grove, around which many of the ancient trees center.

In this area the author found a tree which, at first glance, seemed just like many others that had lost the battle with the elements—all that remained was the stark skeleton, the fine-grained wood denuded and whitened by many years (perhaps hundreds) of exposure to winter storms and summer sun. This particular tree, however, had a single green branch about six feet above the base of the trunk. Closer inspection disclosed that the green branch was, indeed, a part of the original tree that still lived. As if wonders never cease, there was the source of its life in a slender connecting link between branch and the base of the trunk and, of course, the root system. A sketch of this specimen is shown in Fig. 6.

We examined this phenomenon in amazement. The lifeline, obviously, was not something that had grown up after the tree had died; but, rather, was the last remaining part of the original living perimeter that once had encircled the entire trunk. Now the complete circle had been reduced to no more than a very narrow strip of bark, cambium layer and sapwood that somehow had managed to survive, hanging on tenaciously after life had ceased in all other parts of the trunk. Here we had an example of the sacrificial form of life that characterizes this species.

Fig. 6.   A single green branch,
the only part remaining alive, is
sustained by a slender remnant
of the bark, cambium and sapwood that once encircled the
entire trunk. This same principle of life conservation is illus-
trated by the tree shown in the
frontispiece.

Perhaps this one strip was encouraged and strengthened by the need of the living branch and the response of that branch, via photosynthesis, to the moisture and minerals received from the roots. Whatever the explanation, of all the original living perimeter of the tree, here was just one narrow strip of the life-sustaining bark and sapwood that had withstood the bullet-like blasts of hail in winter gales and other adversities severe enough to drive life out of every other part of the tree.

There seemed to be a lesson—or sermon—in this intriguing instance of survival and certainly a striking example of the character of the bristlecone pines that has enabled them to hang on to life until they have become "the oldest known living things."

(For other statistical data on this species see pages xliii and 121.)

CONE-BEARING TREES OF THE
PACIFIC COAST

Directions for Use of This Manual

IN THESE directions reference is made to the "student" rather than to the "reader" because the manual is designed for use more as a dictionary or a field text than as a book to be *read* in the ordinary sense. It is assumed that the person who uses this manual will expect it to aid him in identifying different species of conifers and in studying and comparing their characteristics so that he can recognize them on sight. If he would accomplish this, he should first familiarize himself with the general arrangement of the material in the manual, which he will find in two forms, as follows:

1. A map, keys, and tabulations which group the trees in different classifications. Considered collectively these might be called the general aids. They enable the student to decrease the number of species with which he must concern himself in making final identification of any particular tree. In fact, when the student is trying to identify some tree that is new to him, these general aids should enable him to reduce to a small number —perhaps to only three or four—the species that he will need to study in detail. All the foregoing are in the first part of the book; then come:

2. Complete descriptions of distinguishing features of each species, arranged in a uniform order to facilitate comparisons. The detailed descriptions, 56 in number, are in alphabetical order and are accompanied by pictures of the trees themselves and scale drawings of needles and cones. The major portion of the manual is devoted to these descriptions because from them the student will get the detailed information that will make him really conversant with the different species. This information has been boiled down into what actually will be useful in distinguishing and identifying; endeavor has been made to avoid anything not pertinent to this aim. The pictures, likewise,

were selected with preference for those which emphasize distinctive traits. For example, in the case of the Western Larch a general view of the entire tree showing the remarkably tall, slender shape obviously is most informative. In the case of the Sitka Spruce, on the other hand, a general view would not do at all because it would resemble too closely the general views of several other trees. The Sitka Spruce picture of most aid to the student is a close-up emphasizing the peculiar base of the tree with the much-enlarged butt section and the characteristic bark form.

Before giving a practical example to illustrate the most effective use of the manual, the student's attention is directed to the three keys: needle key, elevation key, and geographical key. These immediately follow the directions, and the student should familiarize himself with them at the outset. A description printed with each key (where it will be convenient for reference should the student need to refresh his memory from time to time) explains the arrangement of keys and how they are to be used.

All the keys list the trees alphabetically by index number, and in the detailed descriptions this same designation is printed on each page for convenience in cross references. For example, when interested in the Limber Pine the student will save much time by looking for its index number, "P-14," whether he is using one of the keys or that portion of the manual devoted to detailed descriptions. The "P" indicates that the tree is a pine; the "14" is its individual number in the pine group.

Identifying a tree as belonging to a particular species is largely a recognition of characteristic traits that other species do not have. Therefore the beginner is helped most by aids that eliminate as many as possible of the similar species with which he might confuse the tree under consideration. The keys are quick and convenient means of doing just this. They are arranged to be used jointly. One key alone may be sufficient for identification in some cases, but more often it is necessary to go farther. An excellent habit in examining some species of conifer new to the student is to check through all three keys and then read the detailed descriptions of those trees which the keys indicate to be possibilities.

Now for a practical illustration of how to use the manual. Suppose that the student is in northern California (say in the

Trinity Alps, south of the Klamath River) at an elevation somewhere between 6,000 and 7,000'. He may not know the exact elevation, but he will know within a thousand feet or so, and that will be close enough. He finds here a cone-bearing tree with needles grouped in bundles of three, averaging 8 to 10″ long. His procedure in identifying this tree by the use of the manual would be as follows:

Turning first to the needle key he looks for the table listing trees whose needles are in bundles of three. He finds six trees so listed. Turning now to the elevation key he finds that of the six, three (Knobcone Pine, P-6; Digger Pine, P-7; and Monterey Pine, P-8) can be eliminated because they are low-level trees listed only in elevation zone 1 and hence would not be found at elevation 6,000' or higher. Now checking the geographical distribution (last column of the elevation key) of the remaining three trees, he finds that one (Bigcone Pine, P-13) does not occur north of district I. So he turns to the map in the geographical key and finds that Bigcone Pine can be eliminated because district I is far to the south of the location in which his "unknown" was found.

Thus, within a very short space of time, by consulting the keys he has reduced the possibilities to two species: Western Yellow Pine, P-2, and Jeffrey Pine, P-3. The keys now have fulfilled their function, and the student turns to the detailed descriptions of P-2 and P-3, where he will find information about cone sizes and other specific features which should be studied carefully to make distinction between these two very similar species.

In addition to their great value in this process of quick elimination, the keys are well worth frequent review to keep distinctions clearly in mind. The manual as a whole, in fact, has been designed for use in the woods, and the habit of referring to it often while examining trees will fix characteristic traits in mind in such a way that the student will become adept in recognizing different species as he sees them.

Once their traits are known, some species can be recognized with certainty even from a considerable distance, though obviously this holds only for those whose characteristic traits are such that they are visible at a distance. After a little study and experience the student may expect to recognize perhaps eight or ten species from a distance by the general shape of tree, the color, the density of foliage, or other sharply distinctive features. Then comes a much larger group—perhaps twenty-five or thirty species—which the amateur naturalist can expect to identify only after somewhat closer inspection and perhaps with the aid of field glasses to note the location, shape, and position of cones. Finally, there remains that fascinating group of fifteen or twenty species which he can identify positively only after having opportunity to handle, measure, and study needles and cones carefully, frequently consulting his reference data to avoid being misled by corresponding traits of other trees whose characteristics are similar.

Since the manual is decidedly not for the botanist, the original plan was to omit botanical names and terms entirely. That was not advisable because confusion would be sure to result if the student had no recourse when confronted with the same names (Bull Pine, Jack Pine, etc.) applied to different species in different localities. This risk of confusion is avoided by using the botanical names for indexing and for reference. The most popular of the common names is always given with the botanical name for the convenience of the student. A very few botanical terms also have been introduced where they will be enough of a convenience to the student to make it worth his while to learn them. These terms, which are defined in the glossary at the back of the manual, and the botanical names are not nearly so formidable as they look; there are not many to be learned; and once the student becomes familiar with them, he will find much pleasure in the convenience that their use will prove to be. If distinction between "genus" and "species" is not perfectly clear, definitions of these terms in the glossary should be studied at the outset.

After a little time spent in study of the manual, trees that the student at first found hard to distinguish are seen to have characteristic traits that were unnoticed before. There is great satisfaction in finding that you readily recognize as friends conifers which were strangers until you learned the numerous little signs by which they show their individuality.

What to Observe

Recognition is based on memory of appearance. With a
little study to acquire knowledge of what details to observe plus
a little experience in applying it, anyone can know and quickly
recognize our native conifers. In this chapter the purpose is to
make practical suggestions on how to go about examining an
"unknown" tree in a systematic way. Experienced observers
doubtless will have their own well-developed systems. The need
of beginners has been emphasized to the author by the meager
information brought in by friends who want to know the identity
of certain trees that they have examined. Sometimes they have
only vague descriptions; their specific data is largely on unimpor-
tant points; and really essential features have been missed
altogether. This despite the fact that there was ample time
and opportunity to observe significant traits plus a sincere desire
to do so.

A systematic plan for observing characteristic traits not only
will help the student identify trees that are new to him but will
increase the speed and certainty of his recognition of species
with which he already has slight acquaintance.

The Distant View

Traits that may be observed easily and quickly are those rather
obvious ones which can be seen from afar. Trees of some species
do not have such traits; others have distinguishing features in
(1) shape, (2) color, or (3) foliage that can be recognized a long
way off. To illustrate by example, typical instances of these
three traits are cited in the following:

1. The shape of the Digger Pine is distinctive in that in 90 per
cent of the trees the trunk separates some distance above the
ground into several major parts of nearly the same size and
importance. This peculiarity can be distinguished as far as the

tree can be seen. Again, the shape of the mature Redwood is distinctive in the graceful, *downward* sweep of its branches. In older Redwoods the tops frequently are flat because the leading tip has a tendency to die out as the tree ages. These two shape features make the species stand out distinctly from among the Douglas Firs with which it frequently associates. Not in every case, but frequently, this shape characteristic will suggest "Redwood" long before one comes close enough for other and more definite proofs of identity.

2. A color example occurs in the cinnamon-red bark of the mature Western Yellow Pine and the Western Red Cedar. This striking color instantly catches the eye because it stands out in sharp distinction from other forest colors. There is no risk of confusing these two species through this similarity of distinctive colorings; the Cedar bark is composed of long, stringy ridges, whereas bark of the Western Yellow Pine forms large, flat plates.

3. Foliage is sometimes markedly distinctive, as in the case of the Digger Pine. This species has long, thin needles that tend to separate and are loosely hung among the branches. The result has been well described by saying that this is a tree that one can literally "see through."

When leaving a tree that has been examined for the first time an excellent plan is to look back at it from time to time while walking away, thus comparing the distant view with what has been observed close up and fixing in mind any traits of shape, color, etc., that can be discerned from a distance.

Foliage

Of the traits that call for close inspection the first is the foliage classification described in the needle key. In examining needles it is well to be sure that the preponderant grouping is noted; this means looking at a sufficient number to make certain that the count used in referring to the key is really representative and not different from the majority.

After deciding (with the aid of the needle key) on the particular group in which the new tree belongs, one can observe many more details on the subject of foliage. It is helpful to jot down the observations in a notebook. The experienced observer will have his own list of items that he finds particularly useful. For the beginner who may need a little help on this point, here are a few suggestions.

If the foliage is scale-like, note whether the pattern is (1) fern-like, *i.e.*, having an "elk-horn" or flat pattern formation as in the cedars, or (2) made up of separate, similar, scale-covered twigs as in the cypresses. If of the second type, note the cross-section to see whether it is square or rounded. Note whether the foliage is soft to the touch or sharp and prickly, also if it has a strong odor when bruised.

In examining needles there is much to be observed after the first question of "number per bundle" has been answered. Note the average length; this is important. For the length measurement do not select needles on the leader, at the tips of branchlets where they are immature, or on the branches where they may have remained beyond maturity. Select needles on typical branchlets where they are growing in the manner that you observe to be characteristic of the tree.

Note whether the characteristic growth of the needles is (1) in tufts, well toward the end of the branchlets; (2) spaced uniformly along the full length of branchlets; (3) in flat, two-ranked sprays; (4) bristling radially in all directions from the twigs; or (5) twisting from the lower side to join those above and thus giving a brush-like formation.

Note whether the cross-section of needles is (1) flat, (2) triangular, (3) rectangular, or (4) circular. If they are flat, are they ribbed and does the underside have a whitish appearance contrasting with the dark green of the upper side? Are they curved or straight, stiff or soft and flexible, and are the tips sharp, blunt, or notched?

Observations of all these points may seem a cumbersome process at first; but as the student adds to his knowledge of characteristic traits, he will associate various features of this sort with the different species and instinctively will look for them to confirm the identity suggested by more obvious traits that were seen first.

The pines—all 17 of them—have needles whose bundles are circular in cross-section. In those attached in bundles of two the section of each of the two needles in the bundle will be found to be an exact semicircle, making a perfectly complete circle when the two are held together. The bundles of threes, fours, and fives will be found to be made up of thirds, fourths, and fifths, respectively, of a true circle. Of the 17 pines only one species has needles attached singly (instead of in bundles), and in this one (Singleleaf Pine, P-16) each needle has a full circular section. Once you have fixed in mind this family trait of the pines by actual observations on needles of several species, you will feel that you have a personal acquaintance with a distinctive trait.

With many species of conifers the student will soon become so well acquainted that no close inspection will be necessary; his recognition will be quick and on first sight. Other species, particularly among the firs, are too similar in general appearance to permit of quick identification, and close examination will be necessary.

Cones

Cones are the most important items in the process of identifying different species of conifers from the point of view of the botanist. Not so with the nonbotanist; he may be unable to interpret distinctions, concealed within the cone, which the expert could find. Another reason for placing less emphasis upon them in this manual is the fact that one who is only a casual and occasional forest visitor may never have opportunity to handle and carefully examine cones of certain species—they may be far beyond reach if, indeed, he is able to find any at all even with the aid of binoculars. No cones of the true firs will be found on the ground; they fall apart when mature, leaving the central spine or stem remaining on the tree.

Nevertheless there is much to be learned from cones, and the student should turn his attention to them after the foliage has been carefully observed. Information about cones should be noted along the following lines:

Do they grow in an upright or pendant position? What is their size? Are they only near the top of the tree, or do they appear on the tips of many branches? Do they grow in clusters or singly? What is the color of the immature cones? (Not all young cones are green; in certain species they are purple before they open.)

If cones can be reached on the branches or if they can be picked up under the tree (cones do not necessarily belong to the tree under which they are found), it is well to note the scales—are they thick and strong or thin and papery? Do the scales stand out in a fully opened position, or are some of them still closed? What is the size of the seeds? Do they have papery "wings" and if so of what size and shape? How many seeds are under each fertile cone scale? (The number of seeds may vary from 1 in some of the pines to 15 or 20 in the cypresses.)

It is a long way from the tiny "berry-like" cone of the junipers to the cone of the Sugar Pine which may be 20″ long; similarly there is a wide range from the paper-like cones of the spruce to the strong, heavy form typical of the Jeffrey Pine. Several species of pine cones have bracts—thin, leaf-like formations between the scales. Douglas Fir cones have protruding bracts of a peculiar three-pointed form that is not likely to be forgotten once it has been observed carefully. There is only one other bract at all similar, and that occurs in a species producing a larger cone. Thus, this trait of the Douglas Fir makes it possible to identify the species positively even from a cone that may have been repeatedly crushed by automobile wheels—despite having been battered out of shape, the peculiar three-pointed bract is likely to be still in evidence and hence an almost certain indication of the species.

The student will do well to look up cone traits for trees of the species that he expects to see on a certain trip and then make observations in the field for comparison.

Bark and Other Characteristics

The bark of conifers varies widely, and bark characteristics should be noted carefully. Young trees do not have the same bark traits as do mature trees, and the latter are the more important. However, in some species young trees have important bark indications, *e.g.*, the blister-like resin pockets just beneath the smooth bark surface of young firs.

When examining the bark of a mature tree, make notations about color and thickness, the nature of the surface (whether firm or covered with loose, scaly flakes, etc.), and whether the formation is in large plates, as in the Western Yellow Pine, or has the fibrous, stringy character of Redwood and Western Red Cedar.

Features of the tree itself are important. What is its general shape—does it have the tall, narrow form of the Western Larch, or is it a scraggly, scrubby tree like the cypresses? Foliage and color are part of the general appearance of the tree. Note any tendency of the branches to turn upward or downward, especially at the tips, and whether the trunk is a single, straight stem for its full length, as in the firs, or has major divisions as in the Digger Pine. The Alaska Spruce, for example, has a trunk that tapers very rapidly just above the ground by reason of strong, buttress-like formations that connect roots and trunk—such traits are important indications. There may be various other distinctive characteristics about the base of the tree: better look and see.

Many conifers have peculiar little earmarks and signs by which they will be known to those who have observed them closely. The gracefully curving tips and lighter color of the Mountain Hemlock branchlets; the rigid, uniform regularity of upper branches in young Noble Fir; and the smooth, lacy appearance of Sugar Pine foliage are all typical of the rather intangible indications more easily observed than described. These traits the student will come to know so well that he will recognize them instantly if he will *form the habit of observation.*

REFERENCES AND ABBREVIATIONS

References Cited

AUTHOR	ABBRE-VIATION	BOOK TITLE, PUBLISHER, AND DATE
George B. Sudworth	Su	"Forest Trees of the Pacific Slope," Government Printing Office, 1908
Charles Sprague Sargent	Sgt	"Manual of the Trees of North America," Houghton Mifflin Company, 1933
William M. Harlow and Ellwood S. Harrar	HH	"Textbook of Dendrology," McGraw-Hill Book Company, Inc., 1937
Canadian Forest Service	Can	"Native Trees of Canada," King's Printer, Ottawa, Can., 1933
Charles H. Shinn	Sh	"Let's Know Some Trees," *U.S. Dept. Agric. Misc. Circ.* 31, December, 1931
George W. Peavy	P	"Oregon's Commercial Forests," Oregon State Board of Forestry, 1929
J. Smeaton Chase	Ch	"Cone Bearing Trees of the California Mountains," A. C. McClurg & Company, 1911
James B. Berry	Be	"Western Forest Trees," World Book Company, 1926
Walter Fry and John R. White	FW	"Big Trees," Stanford University Press, 1930
W. L. Jepson	J	"The Trees of California," Sather Gate Book Shop, Berkeley, Calif., 1923
James Clifford Shirley	S	"The Redwoods of Coast and Sierra," University of California Press, 1937
John A. Lee*	JL	
George J. Young†	GY	

* Attorney (mountaineer-naturalist).

† Mining engineer (mountaineer-naturalist).

Abbreviations of authors' names, with page references, appear at the bottom of pages in that portion of the manual devoted to detailed descriptions of the species.

Abbreviations Used

★	A primary identification feature
′	Feet
″	Inches
Spec.	Species found exclusively in California

LIST OF TREE GROUPS

ALPHABETICALLY BY INDEX LETTERS

(Index in back of book)

BOTANICAL NAME	COMMON NAME	INDEX LETTER
Chamaecyparis	False Cedar	C
Chamaecyparis Lawsoniana	Port Orford Cedar	C-1
Chamaecyparis nootkatensis	Alaska Cedar	C-2
Libocedrus decurrens	Incense cedar	C-3
Thuja plicata	Western Red Cedar	C-4
Cupressus	Cypress	Cy
Cupressus macrocarpa	Monterey Cypress	Cy-1
Cupressus Goveniana	Gowen Cypress	Cy-2
Cupressus pygmaea	Dwarf Cypress	Cy-3
Cupressus Macnabiana	Macnab Cypress	Cy-4
Cupressus Forbesii	Tecate Cypress	Cy-5
Cupressus nevadensis	Piute Cypress	Cy-6
Cupressus Sargentii	Sargent Cypress	Cy-7
Abies	Fir	F
Abies lasiocarpa	Alpine Fir	F-1
Abies concolor	White Fir	F-2
Abies grandis	Grand Fir	F-3
Abies magnifica	California Red Fir	F-4
Abies nobilis	Noble Fir	F-5
Abies amabilis	Silver Fir	F-6
Abies venusta	Bristlecone Fir	F-7
Tsuga	Hemlock	H
Tsuga heterophylla	Western Hemlock	H-1
Tsuga Mertensiana	Mountain Hemlock	H-2
Pseudotsuga	False Hemlock	HF
Pseudotsuga taxifolia	Douglas Fir	Hf-1
Pseudotsuga macrocarpa	Bigcone Spruce	Hf-2
Juniperus	Juniper	J
Juniperus communis	Dwarf Juniper	J-1
Juniperus scopulorum	Rocky Mountain Juniper	J-2
Juniperus occidentalis	Western Juniper	J-3
Juniperus utahensis	Utah Juniper	J-4
Juniperus californica	California Juniper	J-5
Larix	Larch	L
Larix occidentalis	Western Larch	L-1
Larix Lyalli	Alpine Larch	L-2
Larix laricina	Tamarack	L-3
Pinus	Pines	P
Pinus Lambertiana	Sugar Pine	P-1
Pinus ponderosa	Western Yellow Pine	P-2
Pinus Jeffreyi	Jeffrey Pine	P-3
Pinus contorta	Lodgepole Pine	P-4

LIST OF TREE GROUPS.—*(Continued)*

BOTANICAL NAME	COMMON NAME	INDEX LETTER
Pinus monticola	Western White Pine	P-5
Pinus attenuata	Knobcone Pine	P-6
Pinus Sabiniana	Digger Pine	P-7
Pinus radiata	Monterey Pine	P-8
Pinus muricata	Pricklecone Pine	P-9
Pinus aristata	Bristlecone Pine	P-10
Pinus albicaulis	White-bark Pine	P-11
Pinus Torreyana	Torrey Pine	P-12
Pinus Coulteri	Bigcone Pine	P-13
Pinus flexilis	Limber Pine	P-14
Pinus Balfouriana	Foxtail Pine	P-15
Pinus monophylla	Singleleaf Pine	P-16
Pinus cembroides var. *Parryana*	Fourleaf Pine	P-17
Picea	Spruce	S
Picea Engelmannii	Engelmann Spruce	S-1
Picea sitchensis	Sitka Spruce	S-2
Picea Breweriana	Weeping Spruce	S-3
Picea Mariana	Black Spruce	S-4
Picea glauca	White Spruce	S-5
Sequoia	Sequoia	Se
Sequoia gigantea	Big Tree	Se-1
Sequoia sempervirens	Redwood	Se-2
Yews		

(These are not true cone bearers but their close resemblance to them plus the fact that they have leaves in needle form suggests including them to avoid possible confusion in the student's mind.)

Torreya californica	California Nutmeg	To
Taxus brevifolia	Western Yew	Y

Total: 56 kinds of trees, including the two yews

How to Use the Needle Key

I<small>N THE</small> needle key the various species of conifers are grouped according to the peculiarities of their foliage. There are two primary distinctions, namely, whether the foliage occurs in the form of (1) needles or (2) scales. Needles are further subdivided into six groups according to the manner in which they are attached to the branchlets. The attachments may be singly; in bundles of twos, threes, fours, fives; or in clusters (no conifers of this region have a characteristic grouping in bundles of more than five). Finally, to a considerable extent there is a distinguishing trait in the average length of needles in each species, and hence the key gives the typical length range of needles.

When needle grouping (*i.e.*, the number of needles per bundle) and average needle length of any specimen have been observed, reference to the needle key will at once indicate the group in which the tree belongs. These simple observations on the needles of some tree new to the student, with the use of the needle key, often will reduce the possible classifications to 10 per cent of the total number of conifers. Because this long stride toward identification can be so quickly made with the needle key and because even the most inexperienced student can use it easily, the needle key is an excellent place to start the process of identification.

Within certain limits the grouping of needles varies, notably in the pines, and bundles containing two, three, or five needles may occur on the same twig. For example, although needles of the Sugar Pine (P-1) ordinarily are arranged in bundles of five, quite a few threes and twos may be found and rarely even bundles of four. The Monterey Pine (P-8) is the most extreme example of this departure from the preponderant arrangement; sometimes it will have a considerable percentage of its needles arranged in bundles of two. (See note under "Needles" in detailed description of P-8.)

Fortunately for the beginner, in most trees departures from the usual needle grouping are not numerous enough to be a problem, and with ordinary diligence in using the other keys in connection with the needle key he can make his identification with confidence. A safe rule to follow in examining some tree with which the student is not familiar is to be sure to ascertain the number of needles per bundle that is the preponderant arrangement. If this is done, there will be little risk of confusion in use of the needle key, and it will become one of the quickest and most convenient aids in distinguishing the different species.

NEEDLE KEY

CLASSIFICATION BY NEEDLE ARRANGEMENT

Attached singly

		Length, inches
F	All seven firs	2½ max.
S	All five spruces	1″ max.
H-1	Western Hemlock	¼–1″
H-2	Mountain Hemlock	1″ max.
Hf-1	Douglas Fir	1
Hf-2	Bigcone Spruce	1
J-1	Dwarf Juniper	¾″ max.
P-16	Singleleaf Pine	½–2
Se-2	Redwood	½–1
To	Calif. Nutmeg	1¼–2½
Y	Western Yew	½–1
	(Total 21)	

In bundles of 5

		Length, inches
P-1	Sugar Pine	2–4
P-5	Western White Pine	1–4
P-10	Bristlecone Pine	1¼–1½
P-11	White-bark Pine	1–2½
P-12	Torrey Pine	7–12
P-14	Limber Pine	1½–3
P-15	Foxtail Pine	¾–1½
	(Total 7)	

In bundles of 2

		Length, inches
P-4	Lodgepole Pine	1–3
P-9	Pricklecone Pine	3½–5½
	(Total 2)	

In bundles of 3

		Length, inches
P-2	Western Yellow Pine	4–11
P-3	Jeffrey Pine	8
P-6	Knobcone Pine	3–7
P-7	Digger Pine	7–13
P-8	Monterey Pine	3–6
P-13	Bigcone Pine	6½–12
	(Total 6)	

In bundles of 4

		Length, inches
P-17	Fourleaf Pine	¾–1⅝″

Needles in clusters

		Length, inches	No. of needles per cluster
L-1	Western Larch	1–1½	14–30
L-2	Alpine Larch	1–1⅝	30–40
L-3	Alaska Larch	⅞–1⅛	12–20
	(Total 3)		

Scale-like foliage

Cy	All seven cypresses
J	Four of the five junipers
C-1	Port Orford Cedar
C-2	Alaska Cedar
C-3	Incense Cedar
C-4	Western Red Cedar
Se-1	Big Tree
	(Total 16)

GRAND TOTAL 56

How to Use the Elevation Key

THE elevation key consists of tables in which the conifers are classified according to the elevation range in which they naturally occur. The table is in three parts, namely, zones 1, 2, and 3, because three are not too many for the student to use easily and fewer than three would lose the advantage of many natural elevation groupings. In the zone 1 table are listed trees usually found below elevations of about 3,000'; zone 2 includes those which ordinarily occur somewhere between 3,000 and 5,000' (or a little higher); and in zone 3 are those whose range includes elevations above 6,000'. Some trees, like Lodgepole Pine, will be found listed in all three zones; others are limited to an elevation range of only a few hundred feet.

In the zone classification the exact fixing of elevation limits is not intended nor is it necessary. When the student wishes to identify a tree found at a stated elevation, as elevation 1,000' or elevation 2,000', there is great advantage in being able to eliminate quickly all species that grow only above, say, elevation 3,000'. Or, if he is at elevation 10,000', he can greatly simplify his problem of identification if he can concentrate attention on those which grow only at high levels. If a tree occurs in more than one zone, the other zones are listed in the second column of each table; altitude range is more exactly given in the fourth column. If the student is examining specimens near the border line between two zones, he will do well to consult both zone listings.

In the elevation tables the distribution of the trees is also indicated by letters that refer to belts or districts used in the geographical key. This is to simplify cross reference between elevation and geographical keys. For example, the letters A to L appearing in the fifth column mean that the tree is found in the districts from A to L inclusive as marked on the map that goes with the geographical key. The use of the tree grouping by districts is explained in detail in the directions for use of the geographical key.

The elevation range of conifers naturally trends to higher levels toward the South. For example, a certain species that grows best at elevations of 2,000 to 3,000' in British Columbia probably will not find climatic conditions to its liking in southern California at less than 8,000 to 10,000'. It is natural that the farther south one goes the higher he would expect to find those trees which have a rather limited elevation range.

To give the student a more definite basis for placing a species in its proper elevation range, location is also mentioned in addition to the elevation range wherever danger of confusion might arise as a result of the tendency to range lower in the North and higher in the South. For example, instead of saying that a certain species will be found from sea level to 10,000', if the fact is that this specimen grows at sea level in Alaska and at elevation 10,000' in southern California, a more exact elevation rating is made possible by selecting some mid-latitude location, such as Oregon or Washington, and giving a definite elevation range for this latitude. Where this is done in this manual, notation always has been made to the effect that the elevation mentioned applies to the particular location named. The tree then is placed in the table corresponding to the elevation range in the latitude named.

Thus, where the student finds in the elevation key the notation "0 to 5,000' *in Oregon*," he will understand that a certain location is thus mentioned because in other latitudes there will be a different range—lower to the north, higher to the south.

ELEVATION ZONE 1

Conifers found at low elevations: *BELOW* 3,000'
(Including those whose upper range limit is usually 3,000')

INDEX NO.	OTHER ELEV. ZONES	COMMON NAME	USUAL ELEV. RANGE, FT.	GEOGRAPHICAL DISTRIBUTION
C-1	2	Port Orford Cedar	Not above 5,000	FGH; Coos Bay, Ore., to Humboldt Co., Calif. (chiefly along coast)
C-3	2,3	Incense Cedar	1,000 to 5,000 in Oregon	F to L; So. Alaska to Central California
C-4	2,3	Western Red Cedar	0 to 7,500	A to I; So. Alaska to No. California
Cy-1	—	Monterey Cypress	0 to 100	J; on headlands of Monterey Bay
Cy-2	—	Gowen Cypress	200 to 500	J; same as Cy-1; farther inshore
Cy-3	—	Pygmy Cypress	200 to 1,000	I; along ocean in Mendocino Co., Calif.
Cy-4	—	Macnab Cypress	1,000 to 2,000	GHI; forms a "horseshoe" around north end of Sacramento Valley
Cy-5	2	Tecate Cypress	700 to 4,200	KL; in mountains of San Diego and Orange Counties, Calif.
Cy-7	—	Sargent Cypress	200 to 2,500	HIJ; Coast Range Mts., Mendocino to San Luis Obispo Counties
F-3	—	Grand Fir	0 to 3,000 in Oregon	A to I; Brit. Columbia to Ft. Ross, Calif. (a lowland tree)
F-6	2	Silver Fir	1,000 to 5,000	A to G; So. Alaska to Crater Lake, Ore.
H-1	2,3	Western Hemlock	0 to 7,000	A to I; Alaska to Marin Co., Calif. (not in Siskiyous)
Hf-1	2,3	Douglas Fir	0 to 7,000 or more	A to L; Canada to No. Mexico
Hf-2	2	Bigcone Spruce	1,500 to 6,000	KL; So. and Lower California
J-2	2	Rocky Mountain Juniper	0 to 6,500 in Oregon	B to G; Canada to Mexico
J-5	2	California Juniper	2,000 to 4,000	I to L *spec.*; Central California to No. Lower California
L-3	—	Tamarack	0 to 1,600	A; Alaska to Bering Sea
P-2	2,3	Western Yellow Pine	0 to 7,000 in Oregon	C to L; So. Brit. Columbia to No. Mexico
P-4	2,3	Lodgepole Pine	0 to 11,000	A to L; Alaska to Lower California
P-5	2,3	Western White Pine	0 to 10,000	B to K; Brit. Columbia to So. California
P-6	—	Knobcone Pine	1,500 to 3,000	G to L; S.W. Oregon to So. California (in dry mountain regions)
P-7	—	Digger Pine	500 to 4,000	H to K *spec.*; Sacramento Canyon to Tehachapi
P-8	—	Monterey Pine	Not above a few hundred feet	J; three arboreal islands: (1) Monterey; (2) San Simeon; (3) Guadaloupe Is.
P-9	—	Pricklecone Pine	0 to 1,000	I to L; Mendocino Co. to San Luis Obispo, Calif. (also on islands—max. 1 mi. inland)
P-12	—	Torrey Pine	Not above 100	L; two arboreal islands: (1) San Diego and (2) Santa Rosa Is.
P-13	2	Bigcone Pine	2,500 to 6,000	I to L; north side of Mt. Diablo to Lower California
S-2	—	Sitka Spruce	1,000 to 2,000	A to I; No. Alaska to No. California (max. 50 mi. inland)
S-4	—	Black Spruce	Swamplands	A; not south of Alaska in Pacific territory
Se-2	—	Redwood	0 to 2,500	G to J; So. Oregon to Monterey, Calif. (max. 30 mi. inland)
To	2	California Nutmeg	0 to 6,000	I to K *spec.*; Lake and Mendocino to Kern Counties
Y	2,3	Western Yew	0 to 6,000	A to I; Alaska to Central California

ELEVATION ZONE 2

Conifers usually *not below* 3,000' *or above* 5,000 *or* 6,000'

INDEX NO.	OTHER ELEV. ZONES	COMMON NAME	USUAL ELEV. RANGE, FT.	GEOGRAPHICAL DISTRIBUTION
C-1	1	Port Orford Cedar	Not above 5,000	FGH; Coos Bay, Ore., to Humboldt Co., Calif. (chiefly along coast)
C-2	3	Alaska Cedar	2,000 to 7,500 in Washington	A to G; So. Alaska to the Siskiyous
C-3	1,3	Incense Cedar	1,000 to 5,000 in Oregon	F to L; So. Alaska to Central California
C-4	1,3	Western Red Cedar	0 to 7,500	A to I; So. Alaska to No. California
Cy-5	1	Tecate Cypress	700 to 4,200	KL; in mountains of San Diego and Orange Counties
Cy-6	—	Piute Cypress	4,000	J; on Piute Mt. near Bakersfield
F-1	3	Alpine Fir	2,000 to 8,000 in Oregon	A to G; Alaska to So. Oregon
F-2	3	White Fir	4,000 to 10,000	E to L; Columbia River to No. Mexico
F-5	—	Noble Fir	2,000 to 5,000	D to G; only in Oregon and Washington
F-6	1	Silver Fir	1,000 to 5,000	A to G; So. Alaska to Crater Lake, Ore.
F-7	—	Bristlecone Fir	2,200 to 5,000	J *spec.;* only in Santa Lucia Mts., Calif.
H-1	1,3	Western Hemlock	0 to 7,000	A to I; Alaska to Marin Co., Calif. (not in Siskiyous)
H-2	3	Mountain Hemlock	5,000 to 7,000 in Oregon	A to I; So. Alaska to Central California (sea level in the far north)
Hf-1	1,3	Douglas Fir	0 to 7,000	A to L; Canada to No. Mexico
Hf-2	1	Bigcone Spruce	1,500 to 6,000	K to L; So. and Lower California
J-2	1	Rocky Mountain Juniper	0 to 6,500 in Oregon	B to G; Canada to Mexico
J-3	3	Western Juniper	Mostly above 6,000 in California	D to K; Brit. Columbia to So. California
J-5	1	California Juniper	2,000 to 4,000	I to L *spec.;* Central California to No. Lower California
L-1	3	Western Larch	2,000 to 7,000	B to F; Brit. Columbia to No. Oregon
P-1	3	Sugar Pine	3,000 to 9,000 in Oregon	F to L; Oregon to Lower California
P-2	1,3	Western Yellow Pine	0 to 7,000 in Oregon	C to L; So. Brit. Columbia to No. Mexico
P-3	3	Jeffrey Pine	3,000 to 8,000	G to L; So. Oregon to Lower California
P-4	1,3	Lodgepole Pine	0 to 11,000	A to L; Alaska to Lower California
P-5	1,3	Western White Pine	0 to 10,000	B to K; Brit. Columbia to So. California
P-13	1	Bigcone Pine	2,500 to 6,000	I to L; north side of Mt. Diablo to Lower California
P-16	3	Singleleaf Pine	2,500 to 9,000	I to L; dry eastern slopes Sierra and Lower California
S-1	3	Engelmann Spruce	4,000 to 6,000 in Washington	A to G; Alaska to So. Oregon
S-3	3	Weeping Spruce	4,000 to 8,000	GH; S.W. Oregon and No. California
S-5	—	White Spruce	2,000 to 4,000	A; Alaska and east side of Rockies
To	1	California Nutmeg	0 to 6,000	I to K *spec.;* Lake and Mendocino to Kern Counties
Y	1,3	Western Yew	0 to 6,000	A to I; Alaska to Central California

ELEVATION ZONE 3

Conifers found at high elevations: *ABOVE* 5,000'
(Including those whose lower range limit is usually 5,000')

INDEX NO.	OTHER ELEV. ZONES	COMMON NAME	USUAL ELEV. RANGE, FT.	GEOGRAPHICAL DISTRIBUTION
C-2	2	Alaska Cedar	2,000 to 7,500 in Washington	A to G; So. Alaska to the Siskiyous
C-3	1,2	Incense Cedar	1,000 to 5,000 in Oregon	F to L; So. Alaska to Central California
C-4	1,2	Western Red Cedar	0 to 7,500	A to I; So. Alaska to No. California
F-1	2	Alpine Fir	2,000 to 8,000 in Oregon	A to G; Alaska to So. Oregon
F-2	2	White Fir	4,000 to 10,000	G to L; Columbia River to No. Mexico
F-4	—	California Red Fir	5,000 to 9,000 in Oregon	G to K; So. Oregon and No. California; ranges above F-2
H-1	1,2	Western Hemlock	0 to 7,000	A to I; Alaska to Marin Co., Calif. (not in Siskiyous)
H-2	2	Mountain Hemlock	5,000 to 7,000 in Oregon	A to I; So. Alaska to Central California; sea level in the north
Hf-1	1,2	Douglas Fir	0 to 7,000	A to L; Canada to No. Mexico
J-1	—	Dwarf Juniper	8,300 to 9,800 in California	A to J; sea level in Alaska; timberline in California
J-3	2	Western Juniper	Mostly above 6,000 in California	D to K; Brit. Columbia to So. California
J-4	—	Utah Juniper	5,000 to 8,000	I to K; ranges eastward into Rocky Mts.
L-1	2	Western Larch	2,000 to 7,000	B to F; Brit. Columbia to No. Oregon
L-2	—	Alpine Larch	6,000 to 7,000	B to E; Canada as far south as Mt. Hood
P-1	2	Sugar Pine	3,000 to 9,000 in Oregon	F to L; Oregon to Lower California
P-2	1,2	Western Yellow Pine	0 to 7,000 in Oregon	C to L; So. Brit. Columbia to No. Mexico
P-3	2	Jeffrey Pine	3,000 to 8,000	G to L; So. Oregon to Lower California
P-4	1,2	Lodgepole Pine	0 to 11,000	A to L; Alaska to Lower California
P-5	1,2	Western White Pine	0 to 10,000	B to K; Brit. Columbia to So. California
P-10	—	Bristlecone Pine	7,000 to 11,000	I to K; So. Nevada and S.E. California at high elevations
P-11	—	White-bark Pine	7,000 to 11,000	C to K; Brit. Columbia to Mt. Whitney, near timberline
P-14	—	Limber Pine	5,000 to 12,000	B to L; Alaska to No. Mexico, at high elevations
P-15	—	Foxtail Pine	5,000 to 11,500	H to K *spec.;* in the Sierra near timberline
P-16	2	Singleleaf Pine	2,500 to 9,000	I to L; prefers dry eastern slope of Sierra and Lower California
P-17	2	Fourleaf Pine	4,000 to 8,000	K to L; So. and Lower California, in dry mountain regions
S-1	2	Engelmann Spruce	4,000 to 6,000 in Washington	A to G; Alaska to So. Oregon
S-3	2	Weeping Spruce	4,000 to 8,000	GH; S.W. Oregon and No. California
Se-1	—	Big Tree	5,000 to 8,000	IJ *spec.;* west slope of the Sierra
Y	1,2	Western Yew	0 to 6,000	A to I; Alaska to Central California

How to Use the Geographical Key

THE geographical key is a means of classifying the conifers according to their distribution along the Pacific Coast. There are two essential parts to this key: (1) a map on which lines like broad parallels of latitude have been drawn dividing the coast region into belts or districts and (2) a tabulation that groups the species occurring in each district.

For convenient reference each district on the map is marked with a letter (A, B, C, etc.). The district boundary lines are purposely made wide because the intent is to indicate these boundaries in a general rather than an exact way. Widths of the districts themselves were selected with a view to the simplest listings and the smallest number of districts consistent with a close marking of tree distributions. Some districts are purposely wider than those adjoining. For example, by making district J somewhat wider than district I and putting the northern boundary of J at about the upper limit of San Francisco Bay, it was possible to list rather accurately several species in fewer districts than otherwise would have been required.

This key enables the student to concentrate on the relatively small number of species occurring in the district under consideration. For example, if his interest for the time being is in trees that occur in the vicinity of Lake Tahoe (which is seen to be in district I), he will save much time in making identifications if he can turn at once to a listing in which appear *only* those species found in district I. As the list of species for each district is comparatively short, he can give attention to these exclusively and his decision as to identity of any particular tree will not be hampered and confused by the similar traits of trees that grow only in other districts.

GEOGRAPHICAL DISTRICTS

(PART I OF GEOGRAPHICAL KEY)

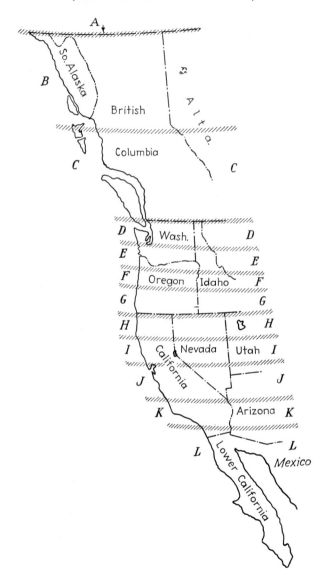

SPECIES GROUPED BY GEOGRAPHICAL DISTRICTS

District A

C-2	Alaska Cedar	J-1	Dwarf Juniper
C-4	Western Red Cedar	L-3	Tamarack
F-1	Alpine Fir	P-4	Lodgepole Pine
F-3	Grand Fir	S-1	Engelmann Spruce
F-6	Silver Fir	S-2	Sitka Spruce
H-1	Western Hemlock	S-4	Black Spruce
H-2	Mountain Hemlock	S-5	White Spruce
Hf-1	Douglas Fir	Y	Western Yew

District B

C-2	Alaska Cedar	J-2	Rocky Mountain Juniper
C-4	Western Red Cedar	L-1	Western Larch
F-1	Alpine Fir	L-2	Alpine Larch
F-3	Grand Fir	P-4	Lodgepole Pine
F-6	Silver Fir	P-5	Western White Pine
H-1	Western Hemlock	P-14	Limber Pine
H-2	Mountain Hemlock	S-1	Engelmann Spruce
Hf-1	Douglas Fir	S-2	Sitka Spruce
J-1	Dwarf Juniper	Y	Western Yew

District C

C-2	Alaska Cedar	L-1	Western Larch
C-4	Western Red Cedar	L-2	Alpine Larch
F-1	Alpine Fir	P-2	Western Yellow Pine
F-3	Grand Fir	P-4	Lodgepole Pine
F-6	Silver Fir	P-5	Western White Pine
H-1	Western Hemlock	P-11	White-bark Pine
H-2	Mountain Hemlock	P-14	Limber Pine
Hf-1	Douglas Fir	S-1	Engelmann Spruce
J-1	Dwarf Juniper	S-2	Sitka Spruce
J-2	Rocky Mountain Juniper	Y	Western Yew

District D

C-2	Alaska Cedar	J-3	Western Juniper
C-4	Western Red Cedar	L-1	Western Larch
F-1	Alpine Fir	L-2	Alpine Larch
F-3	Grand Fir	P-2	Western Yellow Pine
F-5	Noble Fir	P-4	Lodgepole Pine
F-6	Silver Fir	P-5	Western White Pine
H-1	Western Hemlock	P-11	White-bark Pine
H-2	Mountain Hemlock	P-14	Limber Pine
Hf-1	Douglas Fir	S-1	Engelmann Spruce
J-1	Dwarf Juniper	S-2	Sitka Spruce
J-2	Rocky Mountain Juniper	Y	Western Yew

SPECIES GROUPED BY GEOGRAPHICAL DISTRICTS
(Continued)

District E

C-2	Alaska Cedar	J-3	Western Juniper
C-4	Western Red Cedar	L-1	Western Larch
F-1	Alpine Fir	L-2	Alpine Larch
F-3	Grand Fir	P-2	Western Yellow Pine
F-5	Noble Fir	P-4	Lodgepole Pine
F-6	Silver Fir	P-5	Western White Pine
H-1	Western Hemlock	P-11	White-bark Pine
H-2	Mountain Hemlock	P-14	Limber Pine
Hf-1	Douglas Fir	S-1	Engelmann Spruce
J-1	Dwarf Juniper	S-2	Sitka Spruce
J-2	Rocky Mountain Juniper	Y	Western Yew

District F

C-1	Port Orford Cedar	J-3	Western Juniper
C-2	Alaska Cedar	J-4	Utah Juniper
C-4	Western Red Cedar	L-1	Western Larch
F-1	Alpine Fir	P-1	Sugar Pine
F-3	Grand Fir	P-2	Western Yellow Pine
F-5	Noble Fir	P-4	Lodgepole Pine
F-6	Silver Fir	P-5	Western White Pine
H-1	Western Hemlock	P-11	White-bark Pine
H-2	Mountain Hemlock	P-14	Limber Pine
Hf-1	Douglas Fir	S-1	Engelmann Spruce
I	Incense Cedar	S-2	Sitka Spruce
J-1	Dwarf Juniper	Y	Western Yew
J-2	Rocky Mountain Juniper		

District G

C-1	Port Orford Cedar	J-3	Western Juniper
C-2	Alaska Cedar	J-4	Utah Juniper
C-4	Western Red Cedar	P-1	Sugar Pine
Cy-4	Macnab Cypress	P-2	Western Yellow Pine
F-1	Alpine Fir	P-3	Jeffrey Pine
F-2	White Fir	P-4	Lodgepole Pine
F-3	Grand Fir	P-5	Western White Pine
F-4	California Red Fir	P-6	Knobcone Pine
F-5	Noble Fir	P-11	White-bark Pine
F-6	Silver Fir	P-14	Limber Pine
H-1	Western Hemlock	S-1	Engelmann Spruce
H-2	Mountain Hemlock	S-2	Sitka Spruce
Hf-1	Douglas Fir	S-3	Weeping Spruce
I	Incense Cedar	Se-2	Redwood
J-1	Dwarf Juniper	Y	Western Yew
J-2	Rocky Mountain Juniper		

District H

C-1	Port Orford Cedar	P-1	Sugar Pine
C-2	Alaska Cedar	P-2	Western Yellow Pine
C-4	Western Red Cedar	P-3	Jeffrey Pine
Cy-4	Macnab Cypress	P-4	Lodgepole Pine
F-1	Alpine Fir	P-5	Western White Pine
F-2	White Fir	P-6	Knobcone Pine
F-3	Grand Fir	P-7	Digger Pine
F-4	California Red Fir	P-11	White-bark Pine
H-1	Western Hemlock	P-14	Limber Pine
H-2	Mountain Hemlock	P-15	Foxtail Pine
Hf-1	Douglas Fir	S-2	Sitka Spruce
I	Incense Cedar	S-3	Weeping Spruce
J-1	Dwarf Juniper	Se-2	Redwood
J-3	Western Juniper	Y	Western Yew
J-4	Utah Juniper		

District I

C-3	Incense Cedar	P-2	Western Yellow Pine
C-4	Western Red Cedar	P-3	Jeffrey Pine
Cy-3	Pygmy Cypress	P-4	Lodgepole Pine
Cy-4	Macnab Cypress	P-5	Western White Pine
Cy-7	Sargent Cypress	P-6	Knobcone Pine
F-1	Alpine Fir	P-7	Digger Pine
F-2	White Fir	P-9	Pricklecone Pine
F-3	Grand Fir	P-10	Bristlecone Pine
F-4	California Red Fir	P-11	White-bark Pine
H-1	Western Hemlock	P-13	Bigcone Pine
H-2	Mountain Hemlock	P-14	Limber Pine
Hf-1	Douglas Fir	P-15	Foxtail Pine
J-1	Dwarf Juniper	P-16	Singleleaf Pine
J-3	Western Juniper	S-2	Sitka Spruce
J-3	Western Juniper	Se-1	Big Tree
J-4	Utah Juniper	Se-2	Redwood
J-5	California Juniper	To	Calif. Nutmeg
P-1	Sugar Pine	Y	Western Yew

SPECIES GROUPED BY GEOGRAPHICAL DISTRICTS
(Continued)

District J

C-3	Incense Cedar		P-3	Jeffrey Pine
Cy-1	Monterey Cypress		P-4	Lodgepole Pine
Cy-2	Gowen Cypress		P-5	Western White Pine
Cy-6	Piute Cypress		P-6	Knobcone Pine
Cy-7	Sargent Cypress		P-7	Digger Pine
F-1	Alpine Fir		P-8	Monterey Pine
F-2	White Fir		P-9	Pricklecone Pine
F-4	California Red Fir		P-10	Bristlecone Pine
F-7	Bristlecone Fir		P-11	White-bark Pine
Hf-1	Douglas Fir		P-13	Bigcone Pine
J-1	Dwarf Juniper		P-14	Limber Pine
J-3	Western Juniper		P-15	Foxtail Pine
J-4	Utah Juniper		P-16	Singleleaf Pine
J-5	California Juniper		Se-1	Big Tree
P-1	Sugar Pine		Se-2	Redwood
P-2	Western Yellow Pine		To	California Nutmeg

District K

C-3	Incense Cedar		P-4	Lodgepole Pine
Cy-5	Tecate Cypress		P-5	Western White Pine
F-1	Alpine Fir		P-6	Knobcone Pine
F-2	White Fir		P-7	Digger Pine
F-4	California Red Fir		P-9	Pricklecone Pine
Hf-1	Douglas Fir		P-10	Bristlecone Pine
Hf-2	Bigcone Spruce		P-11	White-bark Pine
J-3	Western Juniper		P-13	Bigcone Pine
J-4	Utah Juniper		P-14	Limber Pine
J-5	California Juniper		P-15	Foxtail Pine
P-1	Sugar Pine		P-16	Singleleaf Pine
P-2	Western Yellow Pine		P-17	Fourleaf Pine
P-3	Jeffrey Pine		To	California Nutmeg

District L

C-3	Incense Cedar		P-3	Jeffrey Pine
Cy-5	Tecate Cypress		P-4	Lodgepole Pine
F-1	Alpine Fir		P-6	Knobcone Pine
F-2	White Fir		P-9	Pricklecone Pine
Hf-1	Douglas Fir		P-12	Torrey Pine
Hf-2	Bigcone Spruce		P-13	Bigcone Pine
K-5	California Juniper		P-14	Limber Pine
P-1	Sugar Pine		P-16	Singleleaf Pine
P-2	Western Yellow Pine		P-17	Fourleaf Pine

FALSE CEDARS   C

(*Chamaecyparis*)

The use of "cedar" in the common names of certain trees native to the Pacific Coast is unfortunate because it is misleading. It would be less confusing if "false cedar" had been used instead of "cedar." Danger of confusion can be avoided, however, if the student will remember that there are *no true cedars native to North America.* If this is kept in mind, the designations that include "cedar" will be recognized as merely popular names and will be treated as such.

Port Orford Cedar and Alaska Cedar, both of the genus *Chamaecyparis*, are closely related to the cypresses and share with them certain characteristics. Although the distributions are quite different, the general resemblance of the two groups is close enough to make it worth while to put emphasis on the finer distinctions between them. These are brought out clearly by selecting notable characteristics of the two groups and tabulating them for easy comparison. This is done in the following table.

ITEM FOR COMPARISON	CYPRESSES	FALSE CEDARS
Branchlet section	Quadrangular	Flat
Branchlet arrangement	Irregular	In one plane
Leaf margins	Minutely toothed	Smooth
Cones mature	In second season	In one season
Seeds under each fertile cone scale	15 to 20	4 or 5
Wings of seeds	Narrow, hard	Broad, gauzy
Seed leaves	Three	Two

The four species of false cedar of which detailed descriptions follow are

Port Orford Cedar C-1
    (*Chamaecyparis Lawsoniana*)
Alaska Cedar C-2
    (*Chamaecyparis nootkatensis*)
Incense Cedar C-3
    (*Libocedrus decurrens*)
Western Red Cedar C-4
    (*Thuja plicata*)

U. S. Forest Service Photo

U. S. Forest Service Photo

Ore. Board of Forestry

PORT ORFORD CEDAR   C-1
(*Chamaecyparis Lawsoniana*)

Usual Occurrence:

> Geographical range—F, G, H
> Elevation range   —0 to 5,000′ (zones 1 and 2)
> Foliage   —Scale-like

Leaves: About $\frac{1}{16}''$ long on lateral branchlets, $\frac{1}{8}$ to $\frac{1}{4}''$ on leaders; scale-like, in flat sprays, soft to the touch, in strong contrast with the prickly feel of cypress leaves. Bright green to pale yellow. Conspicuously glandular on the backs.

Cones: About $\frac{1}{3}''$ in diameter, berry-like, clustered on the upper branchlets in great profusion. One to four seeds under each cone-scale. Dark russet-brown, mature in one season. (Cones about same as Alaska Cypress —JL)

Bark: 6 to 8″ thick at base of mature tree, 3 to 4″ thick on smaller stems. Broken into long, loose, narrow ridges. Has two distinct layers. Brown with reddish tinge beneath.

Tree: In maturity 3 to 6′ × 100 to 175′ (max. 12 × 200′). Boles straight, crowns narrow with drooping branches. Mature trees have abruptly enlarged bases. Young trees have profusion of short, "feathery, weeping" branchlets with almost no clear trunk. At first all branches trend upward. As the tree grows older, they become horizontal and drooping, especially at the bottom of the crown. Old trees have clear boles for 80 to 100′.

Distribution: ★ Mainly in a Pacific Coast strip 225 miles long and rarely more than 40 miles wide. Coos Bay, Oregon, to Humboldt County, California. The heavy stand is on the coast, but some trees are found as far inland as the base of Mt. Shasta and at elevations up to 5,000′.

Other Names: Lawson's Cypress, White Cedar, Ginger Pine, Oregon Cedar.

In General: It is the chief species in the area between Coquille River, Oregon, and Point Gregory. Here there is a solid timber stand covering a 20- by 12-mile belt. One of the most valuable woods in the United States.

HH215; P41; Sgt77; Sh17; Su171

U. S. Forest Service Photo

Canadian Forest Service

U. S. Forest Service Photo

ALASKA CEDAR   C-2

(*Chamaecyparis nootkatensis*)

Usual Occurrence:

Geographical range—A to G inclusive

Elevation range   —2,000 to 6,100′ in Oregon (zones 2 and 3)

Foliage   —Scale-like

Leaves: About ⅛″ long; longer (up to ¼″) with more elongated points on leaders. Scales overlap; twigs form an elk-horn pattern. The distinctively sharp and spreading points of the scales, which make the foliage harsh and prickly to the touch, are a feature that easily distinguishes this foliage from that of the Western Red Cedar.

Cones: Small (less than ½″ diameter) spherical, deep russet-brown with a very conspicuous whitish bloom. Four or six scales tipped with points. From two to four seeds under each fertile cone scale. Often covered with conspicuous resin glands.

Bark: Ashy-brown, about ⅝″ thick. Clear reddish brown inside. Large, thin, loose scales.

Tree: In maturity 3 to 4′ × 80 to 90′ or more. Open, narrowly conical crown;★ as a whole; has a weeping appearance due to drooping branches. Branches few and far distant from one another. Exceedingly slender. whip-like leader too weak at its tip to stand erect, so it bends over gracefully, Branches sometimes extend close to the ground. Trunks always more or less fluted and infolded at the base. At high elevations sometimes a low shrub.

Distribution: From southern Alaska to the Siskiyous of southern Oregon. In Washington found between elevation 2,000 and 7,500′. Sudworth gives elevation range as follows:

Alaska. . . . . 0 to 2,000 or 3,000′ (timberline)

British Columbia. . 0 to 5,000′ (latter figure in southern British Columbia)

Washington. . . . . . . 2,000 to 7,500′ (latter on Mt. Rainier)

Oregon. . . . . 2,500 to 6,100′ (latter on Mt. Hood)

Other Names: Yellow Cedar, Yellow Cypress, Alaska Cypress, Sitka Cypress, Nootka Cypress, Canoe Cedar.

In General: Might be mistaken for Western Red Cedar, on casual observation; there is distinction in the "weeping" appearance given by the drooping branches of the Alaska Cedar. For more exact comparisons a sharp distinction lies in the fact that wood of the Alaska Cedar is a sulphur-yellow★ and is heavier by 10 to 12 lb. per cubic foot than Western Red Cedar.

Can70; HH216; P65; Sgt76; Su168

U. S. Forest Service Photos

(Libocedrus decurrens)

Usual Occurrence:
Geographical range—F to L inclusive
Elevation range   —1,000 to 5,000′ in Oregon (zones 1, 2, and 3)
Foliage   —Scale-like

Leaves: Scales overlap, are keeled and glandular on the back, and have sharp tips.   Length is $\frac{1}{8}''$ on lateral branchlets to nearly $\frac{1}{2}''$ on leaders. The scales are longer than in Western Red Cedar; twigs are not so bushy, having an almost snaky pattern.   Foliage as a whole is yellow-green, gives off pungent odor when crushed.

Cones: Small, elongated cones ($\frac{3}{4}$ to 1″ long) more like a flower, each with two seed leaves★ (four little seeds, $\frac{1}{3}$ to $\frac{1}{2}''$ long, two each side of the partition—Sh).   Very different from other cedar cones; pungently odorous. Partially opened cone has the appearance of a duck's bill.

Bark: Cinnamon-brown, 2 to 3″ thick at the base (some authorities give thicknesses of 6 to 8″); can be peeled off in long strips; is highly resistant to fire.

Tree: In maturity 2 to 4′ × 75 × 100′.   Mature trees have rapidly tapering trunks and widely buttressed bases.   "Slender branches erect at the top of the tree, below sweeping downward in bold curves, forming a narrow open feathery crown becoming in old age irregular in outline by the greater development of a few ultimately upright branches forming secondary stems."—Sgt

Distribution: From southern slope of Mt. Hood, Oregon, through California and western Nevada to Lower California.   Common in Coast Range and Sierra.   In Oregon 1,000 to 5,000′.   Western side of Sierra Nevada 2,500 to 7,000′; most abundant between 5,000 to 7,000′.   In southern California 3,000 to 8,000 or 9,000′ (Ch).   California has by far the largest number of these trees.

Other Names: White Cedar, Red Cedar, Post Cedar, Bastard Cedar, Juniper.

HH199; Ch81; P65; Sh12; Sgt65; Su148

C-4

U. S. Forest Service Photo

· 38 ·

(*Thuja plicata*)

Usual Occurrence:
>Geographical range—A to I inclusive
>Elevation range   —0 to 7,500' (zones 1, 2, and 3)
>Foliage   —Scale-like

Leaves: Scale-like, overlapping, frequently ¼″ long, ★ often conspicuously glandular on the back. Branchlets have flat "elk-horn" or fern-like pattern. Flat, lace-like, yellow-green side sprays hang from the branches like lines of fringe. Spicy odor. Mostly persist 2 to 5 years. Foliage is darker green on top and lighter underneath than in other cedars.

Cones: ¼ to 2″ long, like miniature buds resembling a Dutchman's pipe. Have about six seed-bearing scales, each covering two or three very small seeds; wings, about ¼″ long, on both sides of seed.

Bark: ★Thin, from ⅝ to ⅞″ thick. Frequently a bright cinnamon-brown, often weathered to gray-brown. Bark is shreddy and readily inflammable.

Tree: In maturity 3½ to 8′ × 150 to 175′ (max. 10 to 16′ × 200′). Entire bole has conical form due to rapid taper. ★Mature trees have conspicuous basal buttresses which are fluted. A notable feature of the tree is the frequent occurrence of two leaders which combine in forming a dense crown. On young trees limbs curve upward; later there is a characteristic downward swing of long branches with an upward sweep at the ends.

Distribution: Southern Alaska to Mendocino County, California, east to Idaho and Montana. Prefers wet or even swampy locations, though not necessarily at low elevations. Elevation range is from sea level to 7,500′ (on rim of Crater Lake). Usually stunted when found in dry locations.

Other Names: Cedar, Western Cedar, Canoe Cedar, Red Cedar, Giant Cedar, Arborvitae, Giant Arborvitae, Shinglewood, *Thuja gigantea*.

In General: Largest of the false cedars. Indians peel off strips of bark 20 or even 30′ long from young trees for use in basketmaking. Wood is strongly aromatic and is the lightest of all the conifers; 1 cu. ft. weighs only 24 lb., less than half the weight of the heavier woods.

Can65; HH205; P38; Sgt68; Sh13; Su153

SEVEN species of cypress are native to the Pacific Coast north of
Mexico.   All seven are found in California, and only one grows
naturally outside that state.   This one, a species found in the
foothills of mountains in the northern part of the state, merely
extends its range, with fine disregard for the boundaries set up
by man, into southern Oregon.   Thus, cypresses of the Pacific
Coast come close to being exclusively "native sons" of one state.

A tabulation of fundamental differences between false cedars
and cypresses is given in the introduction to the former.

Data about the cypresses are arranged in this manual in a form
different from that used for all other tree groups.   This is
because all seven species of cypress are much alike when trees of
similar age and form are compared.   However, it happens that
unlike most other genera (groups) such as juniper, spruce, etc.,
the genus cypress consists of species whose native habitats are
limited to well-defined areas (arboreal islands).   Hence geographical location becomes a convenient and most effective aid
to identification.   Five of the seven species are found in areas
of a very few miles in extent.   These areas are indicated and
identified on the accompanying outline map of California.   The
other two have wider ranges; but the distributions overlap
only slightly, so here again identification can be aided effectively by a knowledge of geographical range.

None of the cypresses occur in extensive groves; they tend,
rather, to isolated groups.   In the two species that have far-
ranging distribution these isolated groups may be widely separated; in the other five species, confined to relatively small
arboreal islands, the individual trees may be limited to a few
adjacent groups.

All the cypresses have scale-like foliage; all have nut-like cones
much the same in size and general appearance; and all but two
are limited to elevation zone 1.

The following paragraphs, based on classifications made by
several botanists, and with special acknowledgment to Dr. C. B.
Wolf of Rancho Santa Ana Botanic Gardens, summarize what

GEOGRAPHICAL DISTRICTS

little there is to be said about distinguishing traits of the seven species.   Geographical distribution is placed first in each paragraph and should be considered in connection with the accompanying outline map on which the geographical distributions of five of the seven species are indicated.

The seven species of cypress described in this manual are:

Monterey Cypress.................................. Cy-1
   (*Cupressus macrocarpa*)
Gowen Cypress..................................... Cy-2
   (*Cupressus Goveniana*)
Pygmy Cypress..................................... Cy-3
   (*Cupressus pygmaea*)
Macnab Cypress.................................... Cy-4
   (*Cupressus Macnabiana*)
   Also *var:*
   Baker's Cypress
     (*Cupressus Bakeri*)
Tecate Cypress.................................... Cy-5
   (*Cupressus Forbesii*)
Piute Cypress..................................... Cy-6
   (*Cupressus nevadensis*)
Sargent Cypress................................... Cy-7
   (*Cupressus Sargentii*)
   Also *var:*
   Dutton's Cypress
     (*Cupressus Sargentii,* var. *Duttoni*)

W. L. Huber Photo

Cy-1   **Monterey Cypress**   (*Cupressus macrocarpa*)

The Monterey Cypress is found close to the shoreline on rocky headlands overlooking the ocean on the north and on the south sides of Carmel Bay.   This bay, on the west side of the Monterey Peninsula, borders the shaded area marked Cy-1 and 2 on the Cypress geographical range map (district J, not above elevation 100′).   Typical specimens are found along the 17-mile drive that skirts the shore on the westerly side of the peninsula.

In maturity 18 to 20″ × 40 to 50′, specimens very rarely exceed 60′ in height.   Further development made as the trees age takes the form of long massive limbs which finally attain the height of the leader and spread out into a wide, umbrella-shaped crown.   Sea winds may cause enormously developed limbs to sprawl along the ground, grotesquely bent and gnarled. Violent swaying of the branches sometimes produces curious enlargements at the bases of the branches, obviously serving as braces.

This species is extensively cultivated for windbreaks because of the rapid growth of young trees.   The latter have a form entirely different from that typical of maturity; *i.e.*, young trunks are sharply conical and have crowns of rigidly straight branches extending upward in a wide pointed pyramid that starts from the ground.

Drawings of cones and foliage of the Monterey Cypress are included in the manual not because they have any peculiar traits that will be used in identifying this particular species but because the student will need to visualize typical cones and foliage of the cypresses generally.   As the seven species are very much alike in these respects, Monterey Cypress will serve as well as any other.

Cy-2   **Gowen Cypress**   (*Cupressus Goveniana*)

The Gowen Cypress is a shrub or low tree with the typical cypress cones, growing farther back from the immediate shore-line than the Monterey Cypress.   The two trees are found in the same general area, *i.e.*, the shaded area marked Cy-1 and 2 on the geographical range map (district J, elevation 200 to 500′).

Cy-3   **Pygmy Cypress**   (*Cupressus pygmaea*)

The Pygmy Cypress, varying in size from a dwarf to a tall tree, has a geographical range restricted to a narrow coastal plain along the ocean shore in Mendocino County. This location is marked Cy-3 on the geographical range map (district I, elevation range 200 to 1,000′).

Cy-4   **Macnab Cypress**   (*Cupressus Macnabiana*)

The distribution of the Macnab Cypress (sometimes called "White Cedar" or "Shasta Cypress") is not indicated on the map because this is one of the two far-ranging species. It occurs along the dry Sierra foothills from Yuba County to the Oregon line and slightly beyond. Also it extends from its northern limits some distance to the south along the Coast Range Mountains on the western side of the Sacramento Valley, thus giving the geographical distribution a shape somewhat like a horseshoe curving around the north end of the Sacramento Valley (districts G, H, and I; elevation range 1,000 to 2,000′). Distinguishing traits of this species are a conspicuous resin gland on the back or outer side of each scale (leaf) and long, generally incurving horns on the cone scales. (See Sargent Cypress for comparison of traits of these two species.)

A variation of Sargent Cypress, known as "Baker's Cypress" (*Cupressus Bakeri*), is found in the Modoc lava beds of Siskiyou County at an altitude of about 4,000′. It is also reported on Steve's Peak in southern Oregon as high as 6,000′. This variety has short horns on the cone scales: in recent years it has been regarded by some authorities as a distinct species.

Cy-5   **Tecate Cypress**   (*Cupressus Forbesii*)

The Tecate Cypress is known only in two areas, each quite limited, in the mountains of San Diego and Orange Counties. These locations are indicated by the two shaded areas marked Cy-5 on the geographical range map (districts K and L, elevation range 700 to 4,200′).

This species is characterized by its very smooth reddish bark—a trait that is the more distinctive because all other cypresses of California have scaly, fissured, or fibrous bark.

Cy-6   **Piute Cypress**   (*Cupressus nevadensis*)

Piute Cypress is known only on the slopes of Piute Mountain in Kern County, marked by the shaded area Cy-6 on the geographical range map (district J, at an elevation of 4,000'). This species has conspicuous resin glands on the scales and nearly straight horns on the cone scales.

Cy-7   **Sargent Cypress**   (*Cupressus Sargentii*)

Sargent Cypress, the second of the two far-ranging species whose distribution is not indicated on the map, occurs in widely separated thickets and groves scattered through the Coast Range Mountains all the way from San Luis Obispo County on the south to Mendocino and Lake Counties on the north (districts I and J, elevation range 200 to 2,500'). Its elevation range usually is about 1,000', and it has a decided preference for locations where it can find root in the soft rock formation known as "serpentine."

In mountains of the Coast Range north of San Francisco, distributions of Macnab and the Sargent Cypress overlap. In this region the student will need to examine the foliage and cones to be sure of making a distinction between the two species. Leaves of the Macnab Cypress have open resin glands, and the resin, after exuding and hardening, forms little globules on the backs of the leaves, thus emphasizing the presence of the glands. These are not large (about the size of the head of a pin), but they age a frosty-white and hence become quite conspicuous against the green background. Cones of the Macnab Cypress have horns that tend to curve inward. In contrast to these traits, scales (leaves) of Sargent Cypress have no visible resin glands, and cones are nearly smooth.

Dr. Wolf lists a variety of this species (*Cupressus Sargentii*, var. *Dutttoni*) occurring at elevation 3,000' on Cedar Mountain in Alameda County.

Seven species of fir are native to the Pacific Coast. These all
have certain characteristics in common. In fact, "a fir may be
identified as such long before its particular species is determined."

Fir crowns are characteristically conical, often spire-like with
dense, heavily foliaged branches. Usually the crowns are very
dark green, and the branches all point upward. The heads are
thus sharply defined and arrow-like, which makes them stand
out among other trees. The erect position of the cones is unique
and distinctive of all firs. Cones mature in one season. There
are two seeds under each cone scale. The cones of all the firs
fall to pieces after maturity while the stem is still attached to
the tree. Thus one does not find fir cones beneath the trees as
is the case with many other conifers.

The trunk bark, before it is broken and furrowed by age, is
marked by many blister-like resin pockets formed within and
just beneath the smooth surface. This characteristic has given
them the popular name of "balsams" because of the liquid resin
obtained from the pockets which is used for medicinal purposes.

The most certain means of distinguishing the several species of
firs is by their cones. But there are no cones on the trees during
a considerable portion of the year, and every other year they
bear sparsely if at all. Trunk and bark as a means of identification will serve well in certain species, not so well in others, and
hardly ever in the case of very young trees. Hence needles
become the most important means of identification; and in the
firs even more than in other conifers, careful study of needle
characteristics is well worth while.

On all firs needles are attached singly to the branchlets, but
needle traits vary greatly in different locations on the same tree.
It is important to note the very dissimilar form, habit, and
character of needles in different parts of the tree. Leaves from
the middle branches are sometimes different in form from those
of either the upper or the lower branches.

Needles on the lower branches are mostly flat (in one species
triangular), rounded or blunt at the ends (one species is prickly
pointed), and they grow more or less distinctly from two opposite
sides of the branchlets.

In several species of fir the needles are attached on all sides of the branchlets but despite this manage to twist in their bases so that they appear to come from opposite sides of the branchlets only, thus giving the characteristic "flat spray" effect.

Needles on the extreme upper branches are crowded and curved toward the upper sides of the horizontal twigs, giving a brush-like appearance. It is often found that needles near the top of the crown are more sharply pointed than those lower down.

Male and female flowers of firs are borne on branchlets of the previous year's growth in different parts of the same tree. Female flowers, producing cones (and seeds), stand erect on uppermost parts of the crown. Male flowers, bearing pollen, hang below the lower side of branches at lower levels.

The seven species of fir of which detailed descriptions follow are

Alpine Fir...................................... F-1
(*Abies lasiocarpa*)
White Fir....................................... F-2
(*Abies concolor*)
Grand Fir....................................... F-3
(*Abies grandis*)
Red Fir... F-4
(*Abies magnifica*)
Noble Fir....................................... F-5
(*Abies nobilis*)
Silver Fir...................................... F-6
(*Abies amabilis*)
Bristlecone Fir................................. F-7
(*Abies venusta*)

F-1

U. S. Forest Service Photo

· 52 ·

ALPINE FIR   F-1

(Abies lasiocarpa)

Usual Occurrence:
Geographical range—A to L inclusive
Elevation range   —2,000 to 7,900′ in Oregon (zones 2 and 3)
Foliage   —Needles, attached singly
Needles: 1 to 1¾″ long on lower branches, not more than ½″ on upper branches; have conspicuous midrib.   Tips of the needles are notched except on some of the top branches.   Distinctively massed, and pointing upward on the upper sides of the branchlets, those below and on the sides being twisted so as to join those above.   ★This dense crowding is very characteristic.   Foliage deep blue-green.   "Cutting across a needle of alpine fir with a sharp knife will show two resin ducts, plainly visible to the naked eye, having the appearance of *two little eyes*.   These ducts, as visible in this way, are not found in the needles of any of the other true firs."—JL

Cones: When mature, and before swelling and beginning to break up, are 2¼ to 4″ long and about 1¼ to 1½″ in diameter.   They are deep purple, becoming lighter by the time the scales fall.

Bark: Thin.   At most about 1¼″ thick.   Hard and flinty.   Unbroken, smooth parts of bark on mature trees are ashy-gray to chalky-white.

Tree: The distinguishing feature of this species is the long, narrowly conical crown terminating in a conspicuous, spire-like point.   This spearlike head can be recognized at a great distance.   In favorable locations trees attain a size of 14 to 24″ × 60 to 90′ (2 to 4′ × 100′, occasionally 175′—Sgt), although in high, exposed locations it may be only 3 to 4′ high with long lower branches on the ground.   Crown usually extends to the ground, even in old trees.   Lower branches droop.

Distribution: Alaska, British Columbia, Washington, Oregon, Idaho, Wyoming, Utah, and Arizona at or close to timberline.   (Not a native of California.)   Prefers locations where snowfalls are deep.   Endures rigorous climate, and hence goes farther north than any other fir of this region. Elevation range:

Alaska. . . . . 0 to 3,000′
British Colombia. . . . . 2,000 to 7,000′
Washington and Oregon. . . . . 2,000 to 7,900′

Other Names: Mountain Fir, Rocky Mountain Fir, White Fir, Balsam, White Balsam, Western Balsam Fir, Caribou Fir, Mountain Balsam, Oregon Balsam-tree.

In General: Because of the close similarity between Alpine Fir and Silver Fir (F-6) there is need for special care in distinguishing these two trees.   John A. Lee suggests the following:
1. "On the upper sides of Alpine Fir needles there is a whitish color (caused by stomata) which does not appear on the upper surface of Silver Fir needles.
2. "Silver Fir has and Alpine Fir does not have needles twisted at their bases."

HH179; Can54; Sgt53; Su107

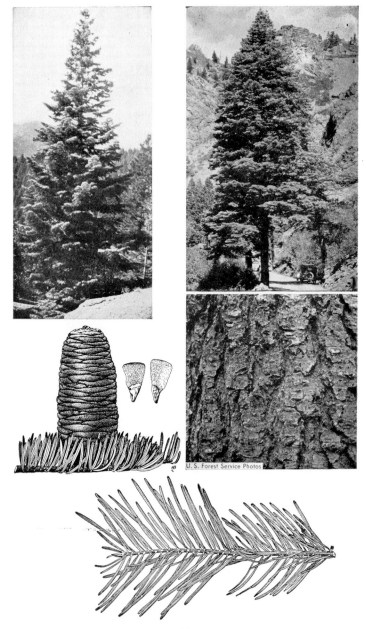

U. S. Forest Service Photos

(*Abies concolor*)

Usual Occurrence:
    Geographical range—G to L inclusive
    Elevation range   —4,000 to 10,000′ in South (zones 2 and 3)
    Foliage   —Needles, attached singly

Needles: In flat rows, 1 to 2″ long, fragrant. Full and plump on the upper side. On the lower branches they are $1\frac{1}{3}$ to 3″ long. Needles of the upper crown are strong, curving, or sickle-shaped, 1 to $1\frac{1}{3}$″ long. Tips rounded and blunt. Unlike the Red Fir, with which it associates in California, White Fir needles have a distinctly *separate* appearance. "To distinguish between *concolor* and *grandis* (F-3)," John A. Lee says, "note that *concolor* needles have a whitish appearance (caused by stomata) on *both* upper and lower sides while needles of the *grandis* have no stomata on their upper sides."

Cones: Stand upright on upper branches, 3 to 4″ long. Bracts attached to backs of cone scales are narrow, oblong, and squarish at the outer end, which has a small point extending from its center.

Bark: Ash-gray bark 4 to $6\frac{1}{2}$″ thick is conspicuously rough with great, deep furrows and ridges—very hard and horny. Frequently rougher than that of any tree that it resembles.

Tree: 4 to 5′ × 140 to 180 or 200′. Branches of young trees grow in whorls.

Distribution: From Columbia River southward to northern Mexico—mainly on west slope of the Sierra. Never in pure stands but often forms three-fourths of a stand. As low as elevation 1,300′ in Feather River canyon but ordinarily a high-altitude tree, ranging from 4,000 or 5,000′ up to about 10,000′ in the South.

Other Names: Balsam Fir, Silver Fir, Balsam, California White Fir.

In General: In appearance something like Douglas Fir, but usually not found below 3,000 to 4,000′ elevation. There is great variation in length, form, and thickness of needles of this species.

HH172; Ch69; P66; Sgt55; Sh9; Su116

Usual Occurrence:

Geographical range—A to I inclusive

Elevation range   —0 to 3,000′ in Oregon (zone 1)

Foliage   —Needles, attached singly

Needles: 1 to 2½″ long. On lower branches, two-ranked and flat, grooved and blunt, with *notched* tips. The foliage is thin in appearance because of the characteristic spreading. On upper branches dense and shorter (1 to 1¼″), tending to turn upward, brush-like, as in the Noble Fir, F-5. All needles conspicuously white on their under surfaces. "In young trees each section of a spray," says John A. Lee, "shows an elliptical outline of needle arrangement because needle lengths decrease toward each end of the section. This test will suffice for young trees at all elevations but is not applicable to higher branches of mature trees or even to the lower branches of mature trees at the higher elevations. In these latter cases the needles usually are more than two-ranked."

Cones: 2 to 4″ long. 1½ to 2″ diameter. Axis of cone from previous year often remains upright on branch. No other cone has this blunt, rounded tip and relatively great breadth of scales. Bracts do not protrude, adhere to backs of cone scales, are squarish, and have a small point at center of outer end.

Bark: Conspicuously whitish, smooth bark earns for this tree the name "White" Fir. Rather thick bark, for a fir, often cut by narrow furrows into hard, sharp, horny ridges.

Tree: Straight trunk. In maturity 3 to 4′ × 150 to 250′. Tops narrow and pointed, crown extending nearly to the ground in open stands; in forests, covers about half the stem. "All of the branches except the topmost have a distinct downward and upward swing." That is, they tend to droop slightly and then turn up at the ends.

Distribution: British Columbia to Sonoma County, California, north of Fort Ross, east to Montana. Decidedly a lowland tree. Best growth in moist valleys and lower slopes. (In Oregon only fir found at sea level; not found in Oregon above 3,000′ and at this height only in gullies and moist places.) In California, according to Sargent, rarely more than 10 miles inland or higher than elevation 1,500′.

Other Names: Stinking Fir, Lowland Fir, White Fir, Western White Fir, Oregon White Fir, Silver Fir, Western Balsam, Balsam Fir, Lowland White Fir, Larch, Giant Fir, Yellow Fir, Rough-barked Fir.

In General: Wood is very knotty and decays quickly—little used for lumber. Ordinarily this tree may be identified by the disagreeable odor of the wood; hence "Stinking Fir." A very stately tree when fully matured.

HH177; Can55; P51; Sgt54; Su111

U. S. Forest Service Photo

(*Abies magnifica*)

Usual Occurrence:

Geographical range—G to K inclusive

Elevation range   —5,000 to 9,000′ in Oregon (zone 3)

Foliage   —Needles, attached singly

Needles: Usually ¾ to 1¼″ long on lower branches.   Mature needles are a deep green—new foliage is silvery, four-angled, plump, and full.   Longer and flatter on lower branches, shorter and closer set near the top.   Branchlets up high, seen from below, have the appearance of having a uniform, *round* cross-section.   To distinguish between Red Fir and Noble Fir, see notes under latter, F-5.

Cones: Upright, 5 to 6″ high (sometimes 8 to 9″ long × 2¾ to 3½″ in diameter).

Bark: ★Dark brown, sometimes almost black in old trees, 2 to 3″ thick (Sargent says 4 to 6″), irregularly divided by diagonal furrows which give a peculiar zigzag trend to the ridges.   No other tree in the habitat of this fir has anything like this bark.

Tree: In maturity 3 to 4′ × 125 to 150′ (max. 10 × 200′).   On steep slopes often bend downhill, the effect of heavy snows which yearly bend seedlings to the ground and from which the tree sometimes never wholly recovers.   Crown often extends all the way to the ground.   The largest of all American firs.

Distribution: Nominally southern Oregon and northern California, though some are found in the southern Sierra.   (5,000 to 9,000′ in Oregon.)   A tree of high elevation, often extending up to timberline in its range.

Other Names: A very similar tree, Shasta Red Fir (*Abies magnifica shastensis*), has the same range and the same needle characteristics and apparently is the same in all particulars *except* that distinction can be made if *cones* can be examined.   The cones of the Shasta Red Fir have extended, drooping bracts, as in the Noble Fir, whereas the Red Fir has no protruding bracts.

To distinguish Shasta Red Fir and the Red Fir from the Noble Fir, John A. Lee says: "Look for grooves on the needles.   Needles of the *nobilis* have a clearly defined groove extending along the middle of the upper surface.   This groove is not present in needles of the *magnifica* or *shastensis*, although all three needles are alike in all other respects.   The Shasta Red Fir and the Noble Fir have cones so similar that it is better to make distinction by this needle test."

In General: Resembles the White Fir but found at higher elevations.   Takes its name (Red Fir) from the bark.

This is the "Silver Tip" or "Silver Fir" of Christmas-tree trade which rapidly has attained great popularity in recent years.   The young trees are almost perfectly symmetrical in form and have upturned, sturdy branches and limbs that can carry a heavy Christmas load without drooping.

HH167; Ch72; P66; Sgt58; Sh10; Su132

Ntl. Park Service Photo

U. S. Forest Service Photo

(Abies nobilis)

Usual Occurrence:

        Geographical range—D, E, F, G

        Elevation range   —2,000 to 5,000' (zone 2)

        Foliage   —Needles, attached singly

Needles: On exposed branches curved to upper side giving very compact brush-like appearance with twig constituting under side or base of brush. Four-angled, pointed, and about $\frac{3}{4}''$ long. On sheltered branchlets or juvenile specimens needles are flat, usually notched at ends, and about 1 to $1\frac{1}{2}''$ long.

Cones: Of compact and solid appearance, 4 to 6" long, 2 to 3" in diameter, cylindrical, flat topped, standing erect on branches, and usually massed near top of tree.   ★Frequent bracts; irregularly notched, with long tapering point protruding and hanging downward.

Bark: 1 to 2" thick divided into flat, narrow ridges.

Tree: In maturity 3 to 6' × 140 to 200'. In dense stands, clear bole for 100' or more. Short, stiff-looking branches stand out straight from the stem. Lower branches often droop.

Distribution: Only in Oregon and Washington—southward nearly to the Siskiyous. Elevation range usually 2,000 to 5,000'.

Other Names: Red Fir, Balsam, Balsam Fir. Improperly but deliberately called "larch" by lumbermen to avoid a prejudice against fir lumber. Noble Fir is in no way related to larch.

In General: The Noble Fir and its near relatives, the Red Fir and the Shasta Red Fir, differ from all the other true firs in having the same or very nearly the same color on the under side of the needles as on the upper side. (John A. Lee says that he never knew this test to fail to be distinctive of these varieties.) The color is a solid, rather light green, usually a shade lighter on the under side. All other firs, on the other hand, have a *decidedly whitish* appearance on the under side of their needles because of the presence of many stomata.

For distinctions between Noble Fir, Red Fir, and Shasta Red Fir, see F-4.

HH171; P49; Sgt57; Su128

F-6

U. S. Forest Service Photo

SILVER FIR   F-6
(*Abies amabilis*)

Usual Occurrence:

    Geographical range—A to G inclusive

    Elevation range   —1,000 to 5,000′ (zones 1 and 2)

    Foliage   —Needles, attached singly

Needles: Usually ¾ to 1¼″ long.   On lower branches flat and sharply grooved on upper side, white lined below, usually (though not always) notched at the ends.   Appear massed above branchlets due to twist in stems. Branches on upper crown have shorter and stouter leaves about ¾″ long, standing erect in dense masses.   Needles on leaders are keenly pointed. [Needle traits that distinguish this tree from Alpine Fir (F-1) are described in notes on F-1.]

Cones: Dark purple cones 3½ to 6″ long × 2¼ to 2½″ thick.   Bracts adhering to backs of cone scales are rounded at their outer ends, narrowing to a long, thin point.   (Cones are larger than those of the Alpine Fir.—JL)

Bark: Thin, smooth, ashy-gray bark with chalky-white areas, even on trees up to 150 years old.

Tree: In maturity 3 to 5′ × 150 to 180 or 200′.   All branches except uppermost droop markedly, those at the bottom of the crown most.   In close, dense stands it is clear of branches for 50 to 100′.

Distribution: From southern Alaska south to Crater Lake.   Elevation 1,000 to 5,000′.

Other Names: White Fir or Silver Fir because of the smooth white bark. Lovely Fir, Red Fir, Red Silver Fir, Alpine Fir, Larch.

HH165; Can57; P66; Sgt56; Su125

F-7

K. A. Meserole Photo

· 64 ·

Usual Occurrence:
Geographical range—J
Elevation range   —2,200 to 5,000' (zone 2)
Foliage   —Needles, attached singly
Needles: Usually 1¾ to 2″ long, thin, flat, rigid, keenly pointed, lustrous needles. Under sides are white lined. Flat sprays on lower branches; upward crowding forces needles into brush-like form on upper branches.

Cones: About 2¾ to 3½″ long and at maturity have a faint purplish color. ★Egg-shaped, bristling with slender needle-like bracts.

Bark: At base of tree ½ to ¾″ thick, light reddish brown, slightly and irregularly broken into thick scabs.

Tree: Mature trees 20 to 30″ × 60 to 100'. ★Sharply pointed, spire-like crowns are so distinctive as to make the tree stand out so it can be recognized from among others while the observer is more than a mile away. All branches droop conspicuously.

Distribution: *Spec.* Scattered patches grow in Monterey County at the heads of canyons and on seaward slopes of Santa Lucia Mountains. Elevation 2,200 to 5,000'.

Other Names: Santa Lucia Fir (*Abies bracteata*).

In General: The rarest of California firs, unique in practically all its characteristics. "The most curious fir tree in the world."

HH182; Sgt60; Sh11; Su121

Four species of hemlock are native to the United States and Canada. Two of these inhabit the eastern United States and adjacent Canadian provinces, and two, Western Hemlock and Mountain Hemlock, are found in Pacific forests.

Typical of the hemlocks are the slender terminal sprays that trail downward gracefully and the slender leaders that droop and nod conspicuously.

The characteristically rough, hard, bark, ridged and furrowed, contains tannin which gives it an astringent taste. When the bark is broken, the color is a clear chocolate-red. Hemlock is important both for saw timber and tanbark.

Hemlock needles are peculiar in having a single resin duct located in the center of the cross-section near the lower surface.

The two species of hemlock of which detailed descriptions follow are:

Canadian Forest Service

1 Inch

Canadian Forest Service

WESTERN HEMLOCK H-1
(*Tsuga heterophylla*)

Usual Occurrence:

Geographical range—A to I inclusive
Elevation range —0 to 7,000' (zones 1, 2, and 3)
Foliage   —Needles, attached singly

Needles: Attached singly, flat, grooved above; have blunt, rounded ends, ¼ to 1″ long. Appear to grow mainly from opposite sides of the branchlets. Mostly persistent 4 to 7 years.

Cones:★ Small, abundant; have few scales, which are longer than they are broad and are coated on the upper surface with fine down. Cones are pendulous from tips of branchlets, ¾ to 1¼″ long. Two seeds, ⅛″ long, under each cone scale, have relatively large wings. Most of the cones drop during the winter.

Bark: Smooth, russet-brown, tinged with red. In mature trees 1 to 1½″ thick, deeply furrowed. The ridges are wide, flat, and irregularly connected with one another by narrower cross ridges.

Tree: In maturity 2 to 5′ × 125 to 160′ (max. 10 × 200′). Small branches pendulous. A tree of graceful appearance because of the fine, lacy foliage. One of the most beautiful of all the conifers. "It always may be identified by ★the drooping tips of the branches, especially the gracefully drooping leader." The base of the trunk often is much swollen or thickened. Largest of the American hemlocks.

Distribution: From Alaska as far south as Marin County, California, eastward into Idaho. Not found in the Siskiyous—prefers wet locations, sea level to 7,000'. Rapid growth on cut-over land makes it valuable for pulpwood.

Other Names: Lowland Hemlock, Hemlock Spruce, Western Hemlock Spruce, California Hemlock Spruce, British Columbia Hemlock, Alaska Pine.

In General: Most abundant and of largest size on the coast slopes of Oregon and Washington.

Sometimes care is needed to distinguish this tree from Pacific Yew (*Taxus brevifolia*). Aids in this distinction are suggested by John A. Lee as follows:

"There is a plain distinction in the decidedly whitish appearance of the under side of the Western Hemlock foliage while the under side of the Yew needles is pale green. This pale green is much lighter than the green of their upper sides, but still evenly green and not whitish like the hemlock.

"Another distinction is that needles of the Yew take to a very sharp point while ends of the Hemlock needles are rather blunt."

HH154; Can48; P35; Sgt45; Su91

U. S. Forest Service Photo

U. S. Forest Service Photo

(*Tsuga Mertensiana*)

Usual Occurrence:
Geographical range—A to I inclusive
Elevation range   —5,000 to 7,000′ in Oregon (zones 2 and 3)
Foliage   —Needles, attached singly
Needles: ½ to ¾″ long, attached singly, but twig formation gives a tufted appearance. New needles are distinguished by their *whitish-gray color*, in contrast to the light green typical of young fir needles. This new needle color gives the tree a "spotty" appearance in summer. Foliage dark to pale blue-green. Needles blunt pointed, rounded, and plump looking. In this respect unlike Western Hemlock, but needles have the same small, distinct stems. (Star-like, in section, instead of being flat, like Lowland Hemlock.—JL)

Cones: Pendulous,* 1 to 3″ long, slender (¾″ diameter), purple before opening, much larger than Western Hemlock, tend to form in clusters. Usually so abundant★ as almost to cover the branchlets and to bend them down with their weight. Cones fall each winter. Some remain on the tree after maturity, open wide, while next crop is maturing. Bracts are one-fourth the length of the cone scales.

Bark: Dark, reddish brown, early broken and rough on young trees. On old trees, about 1 to 1½″ thick, deeply and narrowly furrowed with rough, hard ridges.

Tree: In maturity as much as 4 to 5′ × 70 to 100′ or more. Stunted form on bleak crests. ★Gracefully drooping, slender branches; crown extends to the ground; trunk rarely clear of branches for more than a few feet above the ground. Main branches are unique in having numerous, short, erect side branches. ("Drooping, frond-like lateral branches.")

Distribution: Southern Alaska to central California, eastward to Idaho and Montana. In Oregon at elevations 5,000 to 7,000′. ("Never below 3,000 to 4,000′ in Oregon."—JL) (At sea level in far north, at timberline in south—Su) Ascends to 10,000′ at southern limits.

Other Names: Black Hemlock, Sierra Hemlock, Patton Spruce, Williamson's Spruce, Hemlock Spruce, Alpine Spruce, Weeping Spruce, Alpine Hemlock.

In General: An alpine tree, has little resemblance to the better known Western Hemlock. On high, steep slopes, as a result of snow effect, the trunks are sometimes strongly bent down to their bases, in the form of a sled runner.

* An exception to the pendulous occurrence of cones is sometimes found in the exposed stunted trees, which have been known to have cones erect on the branchlets.

HH157; Can51; Ch85; P65; Sh17; Sgt46; Su95

(*Pseudotsuga*)

THE name "False Hemlock" (*Pseudotsuga*) indicates a relationship between this genus (of which two species are found in Pacific forests) and the true hemlocks. There is resemblance in the distinctly formed needle stems and in the habit and character of the cones. The resin vesicles of hemlock seeds, however, are absent in seeds of the False Hemlock. The latter have the resin pockets, or "blisters," in the bark of young trees, in this respect being similar to the firs. However, they are not firs and cannot be so classed.

The needles have traits that are also characteristic of several species of fir, *i.e.*, flat, blunt needles, attached singly and spirally on the branchlets. Because of a twist in their stems they often appear to grow mainly from two opposite sides and from the top of the branch. Needles of each year's growth remain on the tree usually 5 to 8 years.

The cones are pendulous, borne nearly or quite at the ends of twigs. The most distinctive characteristic of this species, however, is the form of the bracts. ★*No other cones of native conifers with persistent scales have protruding bracts of this shape.* (The larches have bracts of a different shape.)

Not only do bracts of the *Pseudotsuga* protrude conspicuously, but their tips have a strange triple point that is instantly recognized by one who has familiarized himself with this peculiarity. The cones mature in one season and soon afterward fall from the tree.

The two species of False Hemlock of which detailed descriptions follow are:

Douglas Fir... Hf-1
    (*Pseudotsuga taxifolia*)
Bigcone Spruce..................................... Hf-2
    (*Pseudotsuga macrocarpa*)

Asahel Curtis Photo

Usual Occurrence:

Geographical range—A to L inclusive

Elevation range   —0 to 7,000' or more (zones 1, 2, and 3)

Foliage   —Needles, attached singly

Needles: Usually ¾ to 1″ long, attached singly; straight, slightly grooved above; beneath, they have a white band on either side of a prominent midrib. Attached on all sides of twigs instead of in the form of flat sprays. Occasionally persist longer than the 5- to 8-year average. When pulled off they leave an oval scar on top of a small projection.

Cones: Reddish brown when mature, pendulous, 1½ to 4½″ long (commonly 2½ to 3″). ★Three-pointed bracts protrude, often as much as ½″, beyond cone scales. Cones grow nearly or quite at ends of twigs, ripen every year in August, soon open, shed their seeds, and a few weeks later drop from the tree. Cones sometimes grow on trees only 12 years old.

Bark: Thick, soft in texture, easily cut with a knife. On mature trees deeply furrowed. Young trees have "balsam blisters" as do the firs. "The heaviest bark of any tree in Canada, sometimes 10 to 12″ thick."—Can

Tree: In maturity 3½ to 6' × 180 to 200'. Peavey mentions (p. 25) a record-size tree 17 × 380'. Long, clear, straight boles. In open growths carries full crown with great, outstanding branches. Foliage is a fresh green color; upper branches, uniformly spaced, point upward, especially on younger trees, giving the top of the crown a spire-like appearance.

Distribution: From central British Columbia to northern Mexico and from coast to continental divide. Sea level to 7,000' or more. Often in pure, dense stands. In the Sierra of California ranges up to 5,500'; in Colorado to 11,000'.

Other Names: Oregon Pine, Red Fir, Yellow Fir, Douglas-tree, Douglas Spruce, Red Pine, Puget Sound Pine, *Pseudotsuga Douglasii*, *Pseudotsuga mucronata*.

In General: This species has a close resemblance to the hemlocks, particularly in the needles and cones, but is distinct. Douglas Fir and Bigcone Spruce are the only two native conifers with persistent cone scales that have protruding bracts of this shape.

The western rival of Longleaf Southern Pine. Old growth gives fine-grained lumber of bright *yellow* hue. Second growth timber (and heartwood of old growth) is of different character, giving a coarse-grained wood, hard and tough, of *reddish* color. Hence the name "Red Fir."

The one-piece flagpole of the Oregon building at the Panama Pacific International Exposition in 1915 was Douglas Fir, 299' 7″ in length.

HH145; Can60; Ch77; P23; Sh11; Sgt48; Su100

Paul Baumann Photos

(Pseudotsuga macrocarpa)

Usual Occurrence:

Geographical range—K and L

Elevation range   —1,500 to 6,000′ (zones 1 and 2)

Foliage   —Needles, attached singly

Needles: Usually $\frac{3}{4}$ to $1\frac{1}{4}''$ long, attached singly, somewhat curved; grow on all sides of the branchlets, but by a strong twisting of their stems appear to come out mainly from two opposite sides of the twigs. They are more or less pointed, but not prickly.

Cones: Have protruding three-pointed bracts (like those of Douglas Fir) but have★ a size range of $3\frac{3}{4}$ to $6''$ in length, averaging about twice as large as cones of the Douglas Fir. Not all the cones fall each year. Nuts, $\frac{1}{2}''$ long, are dark chocolate-brown, shiny on the upper side which is in contrast to the dull under surface.

Bark: Blackish or dark red-brown; 2 to $5''$ or more thick at base of trunk. Young trees have "balsam blisters" as do the firs.

Tree: Trunk tapers rapidly. Mature trees $1\frac{1}{2}$ to 2′ × 30 to 60′ (sometimes 75′). General appearance of tree very *dissimilar* to Douglas Fir (Hf-1) on three counts:

1. Extremely irregular shape caused by great length of some branches while others are rather short, giving a ragged, scraggly appearance.

2. Grayish-green color, almost "dusty," in sharp contrast with fresh green of Douglas Fir.

3. Branches tend to droop.

Distribution: Southern and Lower California only, at elevations of 1,500 to 6,000′.

Other Names: Long considered a variety of Douglas Fir owing mainly to similar foliage and cones that are identical except for size. In reality it is a distinct species. The common name "Hemlock" is used by Sargent in listing this species.

In General: This tree and the Douglas Fir are the only native conifers with persistent cone scales that have protruding bracts of this shape.

HH150; Sgt49; Su104

JUNIPER   J

(Juniperus)

F IVE species of juniper are native to the Pacific Coast.   Most of
them are small or, at most, only medium-sized trees.   With one
exception (the Dwarf Juniper, J-1) they have scale-like foliage
much like that of the cypresses.   Unlike the cypresses, however,
the junipers have cones that closely resemble berries and thus can
be readily and positively distinguished from the cypresses.

Four of the five species are very similar in general appearance
and require careful observation to make distinction between
them.   The differences are brought out in the detailed descriptions of the several species that follow.

One of the junipers is of such special interest that the author
invited a few comments on it from C. K. Bennett of San Francisco, who has observed and studied it for years throughout much
of its range.   Mr. Bennett says of this remarkable species:

The Western Juniper (*Juniperus occidentalis*) grows to much larger
sizes and attains greater age than one would conclude from reading what
our tree authorities have published about it.   Despite the impression
that this is a drawf tree, the writer knows of numerous specimens that
range from 8 to 10′ in diameter and some are much larger.   One that he
has visited several times (due west of the Sonora Pass, west side middle
fork of Stanislaus River) and has measured carefully, is about 90′ high
and has the following base dimensions:

MEASUREMENT LEVEL	DIAMETER	CIRCUMFERENCE (BARK MEASURE)
At ground level...............	21′ 6″*	57′ 6″
Breast high above ground......	14′ 2″	42′ 9″

* This is maximum; diameter is irregular.

The largest and oldest of these trees are found at elevations of 8,500
to 10,500′.   They prefer south or southwest exposures, are intolerant of
being crowded and frequently the largest specimens grow out of rock in
locations very much exposed to the elements.   The writer has a theory
that they have lasted through the centuries in these isolated locations
because there they have less exposure to forest fires.   At lower elevations some considerable stands of species show marked fire damage and
are rarely of large size.   This suggests that a catastrophe agency
accounts for their not attaining great age at the lower levels.

Geo. J. Young Photo

The rate of growth in the higher elevations is extremely slow.   The writer has cut limbs of 2 to 4″ diameter that show, on the windward side of the "streamlined" cross-section, as many as 400 annular rings per inch.   Altogether there are many indications of great age in these junipers at high elevation; the writer suspects that the one whose dimensions are given in the foregoing may be 4,000 to 5,000 years old.   If this is correct it may be one of these junipers and not a Big Tree that is "the oldest living thing."

The five species of junipers of which detailed descriptions follow are

Dwarf Juniper.................................... J-1
  (*Juniperus communis*)
Rocky Mountain Juniper........................... J-2
  (*Juniperus scopulorum*)
Western Juniper.................................. J-3
  (*Juniperus occidentalis*)
Utah Juniper..................................... J-4
  (*Juniperus utahensis*)
California Juniper................................ J-5
  (*Juniperus californica*)

Canadian Forest Service

Dwarf Juniper   J-1
(*Juniperus communis*)

Usual Occurrence:

Geographical range—A to I inclusive

Elevation range   —8,300 to 9,800′ in California (zone 3)

Foliage   —Scale-like

Needles:★ The chalky-white upper surfaces of these needles; their dark, lustrous green color; and keenly pointed, lance shape clearly distinguish this juniper from all other native species.   The needles are ⅛ to ½″ long and spread widely (nearly at right angles) in groups of three from the triangular twigs.

Berries:★ About ¼″ in diameter, mature at end of second summer (Sargent says third season), when they are a very dark blue—almost black—coated with whitish bloom.   The top of the berry is conspicuously marked by three blunt projections.   The soft flesh of the fruit is dry, resinous—aromatic—and contains from two to three hard, bony seeds.

Bark: About ¹⁄₁₆″ thick, dark, reddish brown, separating irregularly into many loose, papery, persistent scales.

Tree: In Pacific forests barely more than a shrub, less than 5′ high with numerous half-prostrate stems forming continuous tangled masses from 5 to 10 yd. across.   A very unsymmetrical trunk with conspicuous rounded ridges and grooves near the ground.   Only occasionally tree-like with a height of 10 to 20′.   Branchlets conspicuously three-angled.

Distribution: Alaska southward to central California and in the mountains of northern Arizona.   In Alaska at sea level; farther south usually well up toward timberline, particularly in California and Arizona.

Other Names: Ground Juniper, Scent Cedar, Scrub Juniper.

In General: Dwarf Juniper is more widely distributed than any other tree inhabiting the northern half of the globe.

HH219; Sgt80; Su176

U. S. Forest Service Photo

(Juniperus scopulorum)

Usual Occurrence:
>Geographical range—B to G inclusive
>Elevation range   —0 to 6,500′ (zones 1 and 2)
>Foliage   —Scale-like

Leaves: The minute, scale-like leaves on the four-sided twigs and branchlets are arranged★ in four rows of alternately opposite pairs.   The back of each leaf or scale usually has a long indistinct pit.   Note sharp points on scales of larger branchlets.   Foliage is dark green, often paling to whitish.

Berries: About ¼ to ⅓″ in diameter.   When mature, smooth, clear blue in color (from a whitish bloom which covers the thin blackish skin) and usually contain two seeds in a sweet, resinous pulp.   Ripen at end of second season.

Bark: Stringy, has a seamy network pattern, broken on the surface into persistent shredded scales.   Red-brown in color within and grayish outside.

Tree: In open situations 6 to 10″ × 15 to 20′ (sometimes 3 × 40′—Sgt). Bushy with a short trunk and long limbs which trend upward.   Ends of branches and twigs are slender and drooping, giving a "weeping" effect. Often several main stems together.

Distribution: All along the coast in British Columbia, Washington, and Oregon.   Found at elevations from a few hundred feet (Vancouver, B.C.) to 6,500′ (Steins Mountains, Oregon).   Also along the eastern foothills of the Rockies in Alberta southward to western Texas.

Other Names: Rocky Mountain Red Cedar, Weeping Juniper, Red Cedar.

HH223; Sgt90; Su178

U.S. Forest Service Photos.

(*Juniperus occidentalis*)

Usual Occurrence:
Geographical range—D to K inclusive
Elevation range   —2,500' up in California (zones 2 and 3)
Foliage   —Scale-like
  Leaves: Scale-like, about ⅛" long, pale ashy-green; clasp the stiff twigs
closely. All leaves are prominently marked on the back by a glandular
pit, whitish with resin.   "Groups of three leaves clasp the twigs successively,
forming a rounded stem with six longitudinal rows of leaves."—Su. Edges
of leaves minutely notched.
  Berries: About ¼ to ⅓" long, nearly globular, mature about Sept. 1 of
second year, bluish black, covered with a whitish bloom.   Tough, thick
skin, slightly marked at the tops by the tips of the female flower scales.
Contain two or three bony, pitted, and grooved seeds. Characteristics of
berries distinguish this tree from the California Juniper, J-5.
  Bark: Clear, light cinnamon-brown ½ to 1¼" thick.   Firm and stringy.
Divided into flat ridges by wide furrows.
  Tree: In maturity 1½* to 2½' × 15 to 30', rarely 60'.   A round-topped,
open crown, extending in a few feet of the ground. Short, thick, conical
trunk.   Rarely more than 4 to 8' of clear trunk.   Huge lower branches often
rise from the base or trunk middle.   Tips of all branches turn upward, even
in age.   Branches covered with thin, bright, red-brown bark, broken into
loose, papery scales.   On dry rocky slopes and at northern limits of its
range only a shrub.
  Distribution: Southern California northward through Oregon and Washington.   Also found in Montana and Nevada.   In California elevation
range is mostly above 6,000' although in vicinity of Mt. Shasta found as
low as 2,500'.
  Other Names: Sierra Juniper, Yellow Cedar, Western Cedar, Western
Red Cedar.
  In General: A high mountain tree.   Best means of distinguishing from the
California Juniper is by comparison of berries.   However, the uniformly
higher range of this tree makes unlikely confusion with California Juniper
which ranges in a much lower zone.   An exceedingly long-lived tree; age
range may be up to several thousand years.   "Attains its greatest trunk
diameter on wind swept peaks of the California Sierra."—Sgt

* These diameters are greatly exceeded in certain favored locations at
high elevations. See comment by C. K. Bennett, p. 79.

Ch93; P37; Sgt85; Sh13; Su181

U. S. Forest Service Photo

(Juniperus utahensis)

Usual Occurrence:

Geographical range—G to K inclusive
Elevation range   —5,000 to 8,000′ (zone 3)
Foliage   —Scale-like

Leaves: Less than ⅛″ long, sharp, scale-like, pale yellowish green.   Generally lacking the usual juniper pit or gland on the back.   Mostly in alternate, opposite pairs, closely overlapping each other in four rows. Sometimes in six rows, with three leaves at a joint.

Berries: Mature in fall of second year.   Covered with a whitish bloom over a smooth, red-brown, tough skin with a few projecting points.   Usually contain one seed (sometimes two) which is pointed at the top end and sharply angled.

Bark: About ¼″ thick, ashy-gray or sometimes nearly white, cut into long, thin, persistent scales.

Tree: In maturity 4 to 8″ × 6 to 12′.   A low, very short-trunked, bushy or many-stemmed tree.   Near the ground the trunk is divided by deep irregular fissures into broad, rounded ridges.   Broad, open head formed by many erect contorted branches.

Distribution: In California it is found along the Sierra from the southeastern part of the state to Lake Tahoe.   Thence its range extends northeast through Nevada to southwestern Idaho, also in Utah and Arizona.   Generally at elevations of 5,000 to 8,000′.

Other Names: Big-berry Juniper, Western Red Cedar, Desert Juniper.

In General: A tree of the high desert country.

HH222; Sgt82; Su186

Ntl. Park Service Photo

U. S. Forest Service Photo

(Juniperus californica)

Usual Occurrence:
    Geographical range—I to L inclusive
    Elevation range   —400 to 4,000′ (zones 1 and 2)
    Foliage   —Scale-like

Leaves: Scale-like, ⅛″ long, slightly keeled, conspicuously pitted with glands on the back, arranged three in a group on the stout twigs. Leaves on young shoots longer (¼ to ½″) and keenly pointed. Light yellow-green. Die and turn brown on the twig after 2 or 3 years.

Berries: About ¼ to ¾″ in length; light red-brown in color. Markedly different from the bluish black, white-coated fruit of Western Juniper. Skin is loose, exceedingly thin and papery. Seeds are one to two in number, more or less angular, grooved, and ridged. Characteristics of the berries distinguish this tree from the Western Juniper, J-3.

Bark: Outwardly weathered to an ashy-gray color; red-brown beneath— a sharp contrast to the cinnamon-brown of Western Juniper. Though scaly, the bark persists for many years.

Tree: In maturity 10 to 20″ × 20 to 25′. The deeply infolded or fluted trunk★ is straight and less tapering than the fuller, more rounded, and only slightly grooved trunk of the Western Juniper. Branches large and greatly distorted in old trees.

Distribution: Northern limit is in Lake County and Sierra foothills in Mariposa County, thence southward to northern Lower California. Generally at elevations between 2,000 and 4,000′. (Sargent says 400 to 4,000′.) Reaches its largest size on the Mojave desert.

Other Names: Desert White Cedar, White Cedar, Sweet-fruited Juniper, Sweet-berried Cedar.

In General: This species is found at a much lower elevation range than Western Juniper; the quickest means of distinguishing the two is by the fluted trunk of the California Juniper.

Sgt82; Su187

THE three species of larch native to Pacific Coast forests are trees of the north country.   All three extend their ranges northward into Canada, and one, together with the black and white spruces, grows in latitudes as far north as trees are found on this continent.

Generally speaking, larches are tall trees with straight, gradually tapering stems.   They can be readily distinguished from other cone-bearing trees by the fact that their foliage consists of needles attached in brush-like clusters of 12 to 40 at the ends of short, spur-like growths or knobs which stand out from the twigs.   The needles are attached without stalks.   All three species drop their needles each year and leave the tree bare during the winter.   Thus the larches are deciduous, in this respect unlike other native conifers which are all evergreens.

The following tabulation, which is a somewhat condensed form of data published by the Canadian Forest Service, lists traits of the three Pacific Coast species in a form convenient for comparison:

	Western Larch L-1 *(Larix occidentalis)*	Alpine Larch L-2 *(Larix Lyalli)*	Tamarack L-3 *(Larix laricina)*
Bark	Thicker than that of the other two larches	Thin, rarely over 1″ even on old trees	Thin
Twigs	Crown composed of a very few horizontal branches	Branches hang down conspicuously and turn up at ends	
	Twigs brittle	Twigs very tough	Twigs slender and pliable
Needles	Triangular cross-section, 1 to 2″ long	Four-sided cross-section, 1 to 1½″ long	Triangular cross-section, ¾ to 1¼″ long
	Cross-section shows no resin ducts	Cross-section shows two resin ducts, one in each of two corners	Cross-section shows two resin ducts near outside edge
Cones	From 1 to 1½″ long. Pointed bracts project beyond the scales but as a rule not bent so much as those of the Alpine Larch	From 1½ to 2″ long. Pointed bracts project beyond the scale and bend back	Spherical, rarely more than ½″ long. No bracts visible

L-1

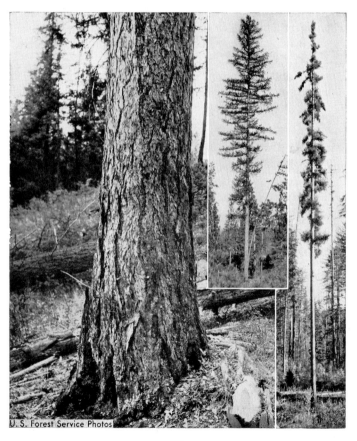

U.S. Forest Service Photos

(Larix occidentalis)

Usual Occurrence:

    Geographical range—B to F inclusive

    Elevation range   —2,000 to 7,000′ (zones 2 and 3)

    Foliage   —Needles, in clusters of 14 to 30

                    on spur branchlets

Needles: Pale yellow-green. In clusters of 14 to 30, 1 to $1\frac{1}{4}''$ long. Turn bright lemon-yellow, and all fall off each winter. Needles are sharp pointed, flatly triangular, and distinctly ridged or keeled on their inner surface.

Cones: 1 to $1\frac{1}{2}''$ long. Soft, woolly, whitish hairs coat the outside of the cone scales below the centers. Pointed bracts protrude. Cone scales broader than they are long.

Bark: Middle-aged and old trunks have reddish-brown bark 3 to 6″ thick which is furrowed deeply near the base where ridges are strikingly massive. Often has oblong plates as much as 2′ long; is highly resistant to fire. Young trees have thin, scaly bark of grayish brown.

Tree: In maturity 3 to 5′ × 200′. Sometimes attain diameters of 8′. Trunk straight, tapering, often clear for 50 to 100′. Crown short, narrow, and open, running to a point.

Distribution: British Columbia south to northern Oregon, east as far as Montana. Usually at elevations between 2,000 and 7,000′.

Other Names: Tamarack, Western Tamarack, Hackmatack, Oregon Larch, Red American Larch, Montana Larch.

                                      HH123; P56; Sgt32; Su68

U.S. Forest Service Photos

Usual Occurrence:
  Geographical range—B, C, D, E
  Elevation range   —6,000 to 7,000′ (zone 3)
  Foliage   —Needles, in clusters of 30 to 40 or more
              on spur branchlets

Needles: 30 or 40 or more in a cluster, more or less four-angled and about 1 to ⅝″ long.   Foliage distinctly light bluish green, turning bright lemon-yellow and falling off late in autumn.   Its color distinguishes it even on distant, high, and inaccessible peaks and crests.   "A cross-section of a leaf shows two resin ducts, one in each of the two angles; that of the Western Larch shows only one duct."—Can

Cones:★ About 1½ to 2″ long.   Bristly bracts of a deep purple project from among the cone scales.   Margins and outer surfaces of cone scales have a fringe of tangled, fine white wool.   Conspicuous, long-tipped bracts.

Bark: Ranges up to ⅞″ thick.   Indistinctly furrowed, has irregular ridges of loose, flat scales which are deep purplish or reddish brown.

Tree: Stunted in appearance, often crooked and bent.   In maturity 10 to 24″ × 30 to 40′.   Some of the branches are large and long, giving unsymmetrical appearance.   In contrast with the brittle branches of the Western Larch these branches are tough and limber.   New branch shoots have a coating of fine white wool.

Distribution: At timberline along continental divide, Alberta, eastern British Columbia, northern Montana, and even occasionally in Washington and Oregon as far south as Mt. Hood.   Elevation range:
  British Columbia........................ 6,500 to 7,000′
  Washington............................. 5,000 to 7,400′

Other Names: Tamarack, Mountain Larch, Lyall's Larch, Woolly Larch (from coating on new shoots).

In General: Strictly an alpine tree—an aid in distinguishing it from Western Larch.

HH125; Sgt33; Su71

(Larix laricina)
including var. *L. alaskensis*

Usual Occurrence:

Geographical range—A

Elevation range —(zone 1)

Foliage —Needles, in clusters of 12 to 20
on spur branchlets

Needles: Scattered singly on vigorous leading shoots, but elsewhere in clusters of 12 to 20.   Indistinctly triangular in cross-section, convex on the upper side with a ridge beneath.   Needles deciduous annually; turn yellow and fall in September or October, $\frac{3}{4}$ to $1\frac{1}{4}''$ long.

Cones:★ Usually $\frac{1}{2}$ to $\frac{3}{4}''$ long, have thin papery scales (about 20), scales twice as long as the bracts, mature in early autumn of first year. Usually fall in second year.

Bark: About $\frac{1}{2}$ to $\frac{3}{4}''$ thick, with rather bright, reddish-brown scales which flake off abundantly.

Tree: In the far Northwest this is a small tree, in maturity often only 1 to $3'' \times 6$ to $10'$.   East of the Rockies and in the Great Lakes country it becomes 20 to $24'' \times 60$ to $80'$.   Trees 10 to $12''$ in diameter are found to have an age of 60 to 75 years.

Distribution: Pacific slope of Rocky Mountains in Alaska, extending northward nearly to Bering Sea.   A tree preferring low elevations.

Other Names: Larch, *(Larix americana)* Hackmatack.

Alaska Larch *(Larix alaskensis)* not considered distinct from Tamarack by many authorities, has somewhat shorter needles, and the cones have wider, shield-shaped bracts.   The range of this variety is restricted to coastal Alaska from Cook Inlet north to the Yukon.

HH120 & 126; Sgt31; Su73

(Pinus)

THERE are some 70 species of pines known throughout the world.   Of this number 34 are found in the United States, and 17 of these, which occur in forests of the Pacific slope, are treated in this manual.

The needles of pines grow in bundles of two, three, four, or five, excepting one species which has needles attached separately. Needles produced in one season remain on the pines from 2 to 6 or 8 years.   Hence the older the tree, the fewer the needles near the trunk.   Needle bundles of all 17 pines are circular in section.

Cones mature in from 2 to 3 years.   Some remain on the trees only a few weeks after ripening; others persist for many years. In some species the cones are attached so firmly that many do not fall after maturity but remain in place and eventually are partly or even entirely enveloped by the annual diameter increase of the branches on which they grew.

At maturity most cones open under heat of the sun's rays. Some rarely open their cones except under the heat of a forest fire. This latter quality makes for reseeding after destruction of a forest by fire.

The seventeen species of pine of which detailed descriptions follow are:

Sugar Pine............... P-1		Bristlecone Pine............ P-10	
(*Pinus Lambertiana*)		(*Pinus aristata*)	
Western Yellow Pine......... P-2		White-bark Pine............ P-11	
(*Pinus ponderosa*)		(*Pinus albicaulis*)	
Jeffrey Pine................ P-3		Torrey Pine................ P-12	
(*Pinus Jeffreyi*)		(*Pinus Torreyana*)	
Lodgepole Pine............. P-4		Bigcone Pine............... P-13	
(*Pinus contorta*)		(*Pinus Coulteri*)	
Western White Pine........ P-5		Limber Pine............... P-14	
(*Pinus monticola*)		(*Pinus flexilis*)	
Knobcone Pine............. P-6		Foxtail Pine............... P-15	
(*Pinus attenuata*)		(*Pinus Balfouriana*)	
Digger Pine............... P-7		Singleleaf Pine............ P-16	
(*Pinus Sabiniana*)		(*Pinus monophylla*)	
Monterey Pine............. P-8		Fourleaf Pine............... P-17	
(*Pinus radiata*)		(*Pinus cembroides*	
Pricklecone Pine............ P-9		var. *Parryana*)	
(*Pinus muricata*)			

U. S. Forest Service Photo

(Pinus Lambertiana)

Usual Occurrence:
Geographical range—F to L inclusive
Elevation range   —3,000 to 6,000′ (zones 2 and 3)
Foliage   —Needles, in bundles of 5
Needles: 5 in a bundle, 2 to 4″ long, attached to all sides of twigs. Needles thicker and more rigid than in Western White Pine; remain on twig through third year.

Cones:★ Few, pendulous, on tips of branches, 8 to 12″ long (rarely 24″), 4 to 6″ thick when well opened. Commonly attached near summit of tree. Seeds thin-shelled, about $\frac{1}{3}$″ long, winged, edible. Sometimes cone scale tips are pointed, more often have scar-like umbo. Before maturing, cones are purple-brown and stand erect. By August of second year they become pendulous. In October scales expand and release winged seeds. Cones remain on tree 2 to 3 years.

Bark: On mature trees deeply furrowed and broken into characteristic "turtle-back" plates, 2 to 4″ thick, reddish brown in color. On young trees and near tops of old trees bark is silver-grey, much like that on young firs.

Tree: Trunks of mature trees almost cylindrical—straight and clear, often for 100′ or more. Mature trees 4 to 7′ × 160 to 180′ (max. 12 × 200 or 220′—Sgt). A characteristic trait which distinguishes this tree from all associated species is the irregular crown★ consisting of horizontal arms of unequal length; frequently the crown is flat-topped. Limbs are rather uniformly clothed with needles, giving a dense, furry appearance to the foliage. This is in striking contrast to the "tufty" appearance of the Western Yellow Pine.

Distribution: Oregon to Lower California. Elevation range, 2,000 to 11,000′ (Oregon). Ordinarily 3,000 to 9,000′; best development at 3,500 to 6,000′ in the North, 5,500 to 8,000′ in the South. Sometimes as low as 2,500′ in California. Never occurs in pure stands.

Other Names: Big Pine, Shade Pine, Great Sugar Pine.

In General: The largest of the pines. Some resemblance to Western White Pine; distinguish by comparing cones and needles.

Ch13; HH57; J56; P43; Sgt5; Su23

U. S. Forest Service Photo

W. L. Huber Photo

Photo by Shoeb

U. S. Forest Service Photo

(Pinus ponderosa)

Usual Occurrence:

Geographical range—C to L inclusive
Elevation range   —0 to 7,000' in Oregon (zones 1, 2, and 3)
Foliage   —Needles, in bundles of 3

Needles: 3 in a bundle (occasionally 2, rarely 4 and 5), 4 to 11" long. Have a tendency to group themselves in tufts at the ends of naked branches. This "tufty" appearance of foliage is a characteristic trait of mature Yellow Pines. Mostly deciduous in third season.

Cones: From $2\frac{3}{4}$ to $5\frac{3}{4}$" long and $1\frac{1}{2}$ to 2" thick. Cone scales have thick tips with umbo in form of short curved thorn on under side of tip; this thorn turns outward, making cones prickly to the touch, in contrast with cones of Jeffrey Pine. Usually set in a mass of needles at the ends of the branches. Cones all fall off before early winter. When open, break through near the base and fall, leaving basal scales on the limb. (Sargent says cones are often clustered.)

Bark: 2 to 4" thick, on mature trees, divided by fissures into broad plates of bright, cinnamon-red which may be 1 to 4' long $\times$ $\frac{1}{2}$ to $1\frac{1}{2}$' wide. Until trees are 80 to 100 years old, the bark is less broken and dark brown to nearly black.

Tree: In maturity 3 to 4' $\times$ 125 to 140' (max. 8 $\times$ 230'). Bole is cylindrical, long and clear, in dense stands. Crown on upper one-third only. Crowns of young trees conical; mature trees usually have flat tops. Branches horizontal or turned upward at the ends. Isolated trees have very long branches, sometimes nearly to the ground.

Distribution: Southern British Columbia to northern Mexico, east to Black Hills of South Dakota. Either in wet or dry climates. More widely distributed than any other North American conifer. Altitude ranges:

British Columbia and Washington....... Sea level to 6,200'
Oregon.............................. Sea level to 7,000'
North Idaho......................... 2,000 to 7,000'
Northern California.................. 300 to 7,000'
Southern California.................. 4,000 to 9,000'
Arizona............................. 5,000 to 8,000'

Other Names: Pondosa Pine, Ponderosa Pine, California White Pine, Western Soft Pine, Black Jack, Black Pine, Jack Pine, Bull Pine, Yellow Pine, British Columbia Soft Pine, Longleaved Pine, Red Pine, Pitch Pine, Western Pitch Pine, Heavy Pine.

In General: Young shoots have a strong odor when bruised. The Forest Service says that this tree provides 50 per cent of average annual lumber cut in California and forms about 25 per cent of the timber stand in that state. See P-3 for distinctions between P-2 and P-3.

Ch17; HH96; J62; P30; Sgt12; Su42

W. L. Huber Photo

U. S. Forest Service Photo

JEFFREY PINE   P-3
(*Pinus Jeffreyi*)

Usual Occurrence:

  Geographical range—G to L inclusive

  Elevation range   —3,000 to 8,000′ (zones 2 and 3)

  Foliage   —Needles, in bundles of 3

Needles: 3 in a bundle, 4 to 9″ long, stiffer and more elastic than Yellow Pine, persist 6 to 9 years.

Cones: ★ 5 to 8″ long (5 to 15″—HH) which is much larger than those of the Yellow Pine. As compared with the Yellow Pine, the Jeffrey cones are much denser; ★they are shaped like the old-fashioned beehive. Prickle of the umbo often more slender than on Yellow Pine but turns inward, and hence cones can be handled without the prickly feel typical of Yellow Pine cones.

Bark: In mature trees reddish to almost black, broken into narrow plates; in young trees, white.

Tree: Somewhat smaller than the Yellow Pine; ordinarily 60 to 120′ and sometimes 170′ high. Has trunk diameter relatively greater, with respect to height, than the Yellow Pine.

Distribution: Through the mountains of southern Oregon and southward to Lower California. Although the elevation range is 3,000 to 8,000′, the best commercial growth is between 5,000 and 6,500′.

Other Names: *Pinus ponderosa* var. *Jeffreyi*, Bull Pine, Black Pine, Pinos, Truckee Pine, Sapwood Pine.

In General: Harlow and Harrar say: "Trained observers rarely experience any difficulty in distinguishing between Jeffrey and Ponderosa Pines in the field. For convenience the principal features of these two pines are repeated in the following table:"

	Jeffrey Pine	Ponderosa Pine
Needles	Blue-green (glaucous in one variety), occasionally twisted, persistent 6 to 9 years	Yellow-green to gray-green, persistent about 3 years
Buds	Nonresinous	Profusely dotted with resin droplets
Young stems	With a purplish hue	Brownish green
Inner bark	Grayish to brownish tan	Light yellow to golden-yellow
Odor of crushed stems	Violet-like or pineapple-like	Turpentine-like
Cones	5 to 15″ long, scales armed with long prickles	3 to 6″ long, scales armed with short prickles

Ch21; HH101; J65; Sgt13; Sh1; Su47

U. S. Forest Service Photo

(Pinus contorta)

Usual Occurrence:
Geographical range—A to L inclusive
Elevation range   —Sea level to high elevations (zones 1, 2, and 3)
Foliage   —Needles, in bundles of 2
Needles: 2 in a bundle, 1 to 3″ long; densely clothe the branchlets.
Foliage of coast (or beach) variety is dark yellow-green.   Foliage of mountain form distinctively a bright yellow-green.   Persistent sheath at base of each bundle.

Cones: 1 to 2″ long, numerous.   Thorny umbo, hooked on scales at base of cone.   This tree produces cones at the remarkably early age of 7 to 10 years.   Cones of mountain form fall freely, sometimes carpeting the ground under the tree; in the beach form (and var. *Bolanderi*) they persist, sometimes remaining attached to the branch unopened for 15 to 20 years or more.

Bark: Bark of beach and mountain forms differ: in the beach form it is ¾ to 1″ thick, deeply furrowed and transversely fissured, reddish brown to black, only superficially scaly.   The mountain form has bark only ¼″ thick, often a light brown to orange color and scaly to the point of being scabby, even near the top and on young trees.

Tree: Beach form often is diminutive, scrubby, and distorted.   The mountain form of mature tree is 12 to 18″ × 90′ (max. 6 × 150′).   Inland form has tall slender bole, rounded crown.   Much-forked branches often extend nearly to base of stem.

Distribution: From Alaska to northern part of Lower California.   Eastward to the Dakotas.   Sea level to 11,000′ (in southern territory).   Most often on the edges of mountain meadows.   Occurs in pure stands of dense forests, also mixes with other trees.   "Attains greatest size and development in southern Sierra Nevada at elevations between 8,000 and 9,500′."—Sgt

Other Names: Beach form: Beach Pine, Sand Pine, Scrub Pine, Tamarack Pine, Knotty Pine, Henderson's Pine.   (In the area of the Mendocino coastal plain known as the "White Plains," the Beach Pine is replaced by a dwarf variety, generally less than 5′ tall, known as *Pinus contorta* var. *Bolanderi* or Bolander's Pine.)

Mountain form: *Pinus contorta* var. *Murrayana* or var. *Latifolia*, *Pinus Murrayana*, Tamarack, Spruce Pine, Murray Pine.

In General: Beach and mountain forms of *Pinus contorta* are not really separable; Sudworth says that those who attempt it "would have taken the broader view had they been able to study the trees as they grow in all their retreats."   All differences "are not too great to be consistently merged in one polymorphous species."

Ch37; HH105; Sgt23; Sh7; Su49; P45

U.S. Forest Service Photo

(*Pinus monticola*)

Usual Occurrence:
    Geographical range—B to K inclusive
    Elevation range   —Sea level to 10,000' (zones 1, 2, and 3)
    Foliage   —Needles, in bundles of 5
Needles: 5 in a bundle, rarely 4.   1 to 4″ long, pointed, very slender. Shorter than those of Sugar Pine.   Sheathed at base by thinnish, narrow, deciduous scales, some of which are shorter than those of the Sugar Pine.

    Cones: 6 to 8 and rarely 10″ long ("up to 18″ "—Can).   In clusters of one to seven, borne near the ends of high branches, pendulous, on long stalks. ★Very slender when closed and usually curved toward the tip.   Scales thin, smooth, widening from the base to the rounded apex.   A terminal, scar-like umbo.   Cones similar to but smaller than Sugar Pine cones.   Two seeds, about ⅓″ long, under each cone scale.   Seed wings are sharper pointed than those of the Sugar Pine.

    Bark: On mature trees broken into small square blocks; ¾ to 1¼″ thick. Color varies from cinnamon in open stands to grayish purple in dense forests. Divided into small, nearly square plates by deep longitudinal and cross fissures—covered with small scales.

    Tree: In maturity 2 to 3′ × 100′ or more (4 to 8′ × 150′—Sgt).   Tall, slender bole peculiarly short branched; narrow, symmetrical crown with slender branches, horizontal or somewhat drooping.   Very top may have a cluster of ascending or semi-upright cone-bearing branches.   Usually one or several stout branches extend horizontally 10 to 15′ beyond other branches. This peculiarity is visible as far as the tree can be seen.

    Distribution: Nowhere abundant except in small patches.   This tree is primarily a mountain type, but in the Puget Sound basin and the Olympic Peninsula it occurs frequently at sea level.   Elevation range is as follows:

British Columbia, Washington, and Oregon, west of the Cascades...............................	Sea level to 3,000'
East of the Cascades and in Idaho and Montana......	2,000 to 7,000'
California.......................................	5,000 to 10,000'

    Other Names: Silver Pine, White Pine, Idaho White Pine, Mountain White Pine, Mountain Pine, Little Sugar Pine, Soft Pine, Fingercone Pine, Mountain Weymouth Pine.

    In General: A tree in many of its characteristics similar to Sugar Pine. Age ranges from 200 to 500 years.   "Snow falls throughout its range." Very young twigs and shoots are covered with a fine reddish down which helps to distinguish this tree from similar species.

Ch41; HH54; J56; Sgt4; Sh7; Su20; P47

(Pinus attenuata)

Usual Occurrence:

> Geographical range—G to L inclusive
> Elevation range   —1,500 to 4,000′ (zone 1)
> Foliage   —Needles, in bundles of 3

Needles: 3 in a bundle, 3 to 7″ long (mainly 3½ to 5″). Slender, rigid, light green.

Cones: 3 to 6″ long, slender; scales moderately thickened at tip except on outside at base where they are raised into conspicuous rounded or pointed knobs. Cones adhere to the branches indefinitely, seldom opening until the tree is killed. ★"Clusters of them, rigidly attached and bent down, encircle the main stems of even small trees (5 to 8′ high) and are the most striking characteristics of this pine." Umbos small and slender; prickles usually deciduous.

Bark: Thin (¼ to ½″ thick), dull brown, shallowly ridged and furrowed, mainly near the ground. The ridges have large loose scales.

Tree: In maturity 6 to 12″ × 15 to 30′. Exceptional trees, 20″ × 80′. The slender branches curve outward and upward. Old trees often have the trunk forked near its middle. Branches of young trees are attached to the trunk in regular whorls.

Distribution: Southwestern Oregon to southern California. Elevation range, 1,500 to 4,000′ on rocky slopes and ridges in the most hopelessly inhospitable and desolate mountain regions.

Other Names: Scrub Pine (*Pinus tuberculata*).

In General: Valued chiefly as a ground cover following forest fires because cones usually do not open until the death of the tree. Many trees show that they have retained their cones for nearly 50 years.

Ch33; HH112; J77; P66; Sgt19; Sh7; Su62

P-7

(*Pinus Sabiniana*)

Usual Occurrence:
Geographical range—H, I, J, K
Elevation range   —1,000 to 4,000' (zone 1)
Foliage   —Needles, in bundles of 3

Needles: In bundles of 3. 7 to 13½" long, drooping. Gray-green in color and sparse. ★"You can fairly see through a Digger Pine." Needles fall usually in third and fourth years.

Cones: 6 to 10" long, 5 to 7" thick, on stalks about 2" long. Mature in second season, but remain on tree 1 to 7 years after releasing the seeds, which are very hard shelled and about ¾" long. Some cone scale tips develop into triangular hooks. When cones fall, a few scales from base usually remain on the stalk. Cones frequently have pitch on scale tips.

Bark: Mature trees have bark 1½ to 2" thick: dull gray-brown, scaly, deeply ridged, fissures slightly tinged with red.

Tree: 1 to 4' × 40 to 50', sometimes 90'. Trunk usually branches, 5 to 15' from the ground, into a cluster of secondary stems which form a broom-like top. One rarely sees a tree in which trunk axis bears only lateral branches through the crown.

Distribution: *Spec.* In the dry, hot foothills of central California. Usual elevation range 500 to 4,000'. Always in scattered growths. Ranges south to the Tehachapi and north to Sacramento River canyon.

Other Names: Sabin's Pine, Bull Pine, Squaw Pine, Nut Pine, Gray Pine, Grayleaf Pine, Blue Pine.

In General: The gray, thin foliaged crown of one or two long upright forks, with big, dark cones that can be seen half a mile away, distinguish it at long distances from associated trees. When planted for ornament in rich, culti-vated soil, the foliage becomes much stouter and thicker, giving the tree an entirely different aspect from one grown in its dry native habitat; the cones of such cultivated trees are usually smaller. It is named after the Digger Indians of California who used the seed for food.

Ch29; HH110; J68; Sgt20; Sh3; Su54

(*Pinus radiata*)

Usual Occurrence:
   Geographical range—J
   Elevation range   —A few hundred feet above sea level (zone 1)
   Foliage   —Needles, in bundles of 3
   Needles: Bundles of 3 and 2, from 3 to 6″ long.   Make a rich, dark green foliage.   Deciduous in third season.
   Several hundred foliage samples of this species, examined by the author, had many of the needles attached in bundles of 2; in some samples the 2 needle bundles constituted 75 per cent of the total.   Needle grouping is not a stable and dependable trait in this tree.
   Cones: 3 to 7″ long.   Frequently curved.   Scales on outer side near base conspicuously developed or swollen at tip with pyramidal tubercle armed with prickle which usually weathers off.   Closed★ cones persist for many years on the tree.   Scales of reflexed cones have flat smooth edges.
   Bark: Roughly fissured, 1½ to 2″ thick, hard, and more nearly black than that of any other California pine.
   Tree: In maturity 1 to 4′ × 90 to 100′ in sheltered locations.   (60 to 80′ high on coast, where it is distorted and flat topped.)
   Distribution: Not found more than a few hundred feet above sea level, then only in a few limited areas of central California, particularly near Monterey and San Simeon.   A closely allied form (var. *binnata*) occurs on Guadalupe Island, Lower California.   This variety has most of its leaves in bundles of two.
   Other Names: *Pinus insignis.*
   In General: Much used for windbreak and cover in San Francisco Bay region.   Wider horticultural distribution than any other California conifer. A short-lived tree.   Maturity usually 80 to 100 years and rarely passing the age of 150 years.

HH114; J76; Sgt19; Sh4; Su58

Usual Occurrence:

Geographical range—I to L inclusive

Elevation range   —0 to 1,000' (zone 1)

Foliage   —Needles, in bundles of 2

Needles: 2 in a bundle, $3\frac{1}{2}$ to $5\frac{1}{2}''$ long, stiff, deep yellow-green. Begin to fall in second year. Foliage is conspicuously dense on the extremities of the numerous branches.

Cones: 2 to $3\frac{1}{2}''$ long, attached at a sharp angle, thus making lack of symmetry a characteristic trait; usually in clusters. Scales much thickened on outside of cone and at base often armed with spur-like spines. The cones are characterized by their indefinite persistence. A singular fact is that they rarely or never are imbedded in the stems of the trees, as is the case of other pines with persistent cones. The stems of the cones are soon broken by the growing branch, and thereafter the cone is held lightly by the living bark. Seeds, nearly triangular, have a roughish surface.

Bark: 4 to 6'' thick, deeply furrowed and rough, with purple-brown scales.

Tree: In maturity 1 to 2' × 30 to 60' (max. 3 × 80'). A dense crown, rounded at the top, with stout branches extending to the ground.

Distribution: California coast region from Mendocino County to San Luis Obispo County, also Lower California coast and Cedros Island. From near sea level to elevation of 1,000' and extending about 1 mile inland.

Other Names: Bishop's Pine, Swamp Pine, Dwarf Marine Pine, Obispo Pine, Bull Pine, Scrub Pine.

In General: On Santa Cruz Island (30 miles offshore at Santa Barbara) two pines are found. One is the typical Pricklecone Pine with unsymmetrical cones whose scale tips are thickened. The other, a closely related species, differs in having *symmetrical* cones with all the cone scales *flat*. This latter pine has been named *Pinus remorata*.

HH115; Sgt28; Sh7; Su65

C. W. Ferguson Photo

(*Pinus aristata*)

Usual Occurrence:

Geographical range—I, J, K
Elevation range   —7,000 to 11,600′ (zone 3)
Foliage   —Needles, in bundles of 5

Needles: Usually 5 to a bundle, 1¼ to 1½″ long, attached in clusters, Deep green foliage, densely clustered at ends of twigs in long, compact, brush-like tufts.

Cones: Usually 2½ to 3½″ long. Scales tipped with long, sharp, thin★ prickles. Hang pendant on very tips of branchlets. Open and scatter seeds about Oct. 1 of second year.

Bark: Thin on young trees. On old trees ½ to ¾″ thick, dull reddish brown, shallowly furrowed; the main flat ridges irregularly connected by narrower slanting divisions. Surface covered with small scales.

Tree: In maturity 12 to 24″ × 20 to 40′. An irregular bushy tree with a short, thick trunk. Short, stout branches in regular whorls while young.

Distribution: Found mainly at high elevations (7,000 to 11,600′). Colorado, southern Utah, southern Nevada, and southeastern California, on San Francisco peaks in northern Arizona and in New Mexico. In California reported locations are Panamint Mountains (7,800 to 10,800′), and in the White and Inyo Mountains.

Other Names: Foxtail Pine, Hickory Pine.

In General: An alpine species; found in scattered stands and at high elevations.

Ch57;HH71;Sgt8;Sh5;Su37

Since discovery of the great age of bristlecone pines, intensive study has been devoted to this species so that new and additional information, not available for earlier printings of this book, can now be included in this 1965 printing. See the color-plate frontispiece, Figs. 5 and 6 and pages lii to lvii inclusive.

Geo. D. Whittle Photo

U. S. Forest Service Photo

(Pinus albicaulis)

Usual Occurrence:

Geographical range—C to K inclusive

Elevation range   —5,000 to 12,000′ (zone 3)

Foliage   —Needles, in bundles of 5

Needles: In bundles of 5, from 1 to 2½″ long, stout, rigid, slightly incurving, dark green, persisting 5 to 8 years but clothing only the tips of the slowly growing branchlets.

Cones: Deep purple when growing on the tree, brown when dry, very thick scales. 1 to 3″ long and nearly as thick (ovoid or subglobose, short, acute umbo). Needles and cones cluster at ends of branches. Cones remain closed and retain the seeds for several years.

Bark: Thin and silvery, rarely more than ½″ thick. (Young tree bark is pinkish.—GY) Some old trees in exposed locations have light reddish bark. At the base narrow cracks break the bark into whitish scales.

Tree: Dwarfed into shapeless shrubs at highest elevations but in more sheltered spots have been found 2′ in diameter and 50′ high (2 to 4′ × 60′ as a maximum.—Sgt). Dwarf trees often have two or three main stems from the base and often crowns on the ground like low, flat tables over which one may walk readily.

Distribution: High Sierra passes, usually at or near timberline. 5,000 to 11,000′ in northern ranges and 9,500 to 12,000′ in the south. Not below elevation 7,500′ on Rubicon Peak near Lake Tahoe, California. Southwest limit about Mt. Whitney. North into British Columbia and east into Montana.

Other Names: Dwarf Pine, White-stemmed Pine, Scrub Pine.

In General: Catkins bright pink. Reproduction is always poor; growth is very slow; maturity is reached in about 250 years, but trees live to much greater age.

Ch53; HH63; J58; Sgt6; Sh7; Su30

P-12

Geo. D. Whittle Photo

U. S. Forest Service Photo

· 124 ·

(*Pinus Torreyana*)

Usual Occurrence:

        Geographical range—L

        Elevation range   —0 to 100' (zone 1)

        Foliage   —Needles, in bundles of 5

Needles: In bundles of 5, from 8 to 12″ long, thick, stiff, and strong; have sharp points. Stand out from all sides of branches, giving boughs a stiff, coarse appearance. Because needles do not persist long, the foliage tends to cluster around bough tips thus giving a tufted appearance to branch ends. The young needles have a remarkably long sheath at their base ($1\frac{1}{4}$″ or more), light brown in color. When needles are old, the sheath turns darker (almost black) and has a tendency to be torn and ragged at its outer end.

Cones: 4 to 6″ long, subglobose, on long stalks. Russet or chocolate-brown, strongly attached; scales at apex thickened into heavy pyramids, armed with small spines. Mostly deciduous in fourth year. Seeds $\frac{3}{4}$ to 1″ long, edible raw or roasted.

Bark: About 1″ thick, roughly and deeply broken into ridges with wide, flat, pale reddish-brown scales.

Tree: Bent by sea winds. In maturity a crooked tree of irregular shape, 8 to 14″ × 20 to 35′. Sheltered spots sometimes produce a tree 50 to 60′ high.

Distribution: *Spec.* Found near the sea only in San Diego County and Santa Rosa Island. (Sea level to about 100'.)

Other Names: Soledad Pine, Del Mar Pine, Lone Pine.

In General: The rarest of California pines. ★Its only known occurrence on the mainland is in San Diego County near the mouth of the Soledad River, now protected in an extensive municipal park.

HH113; J70; Sgt30; Sh7; Su41

P-13

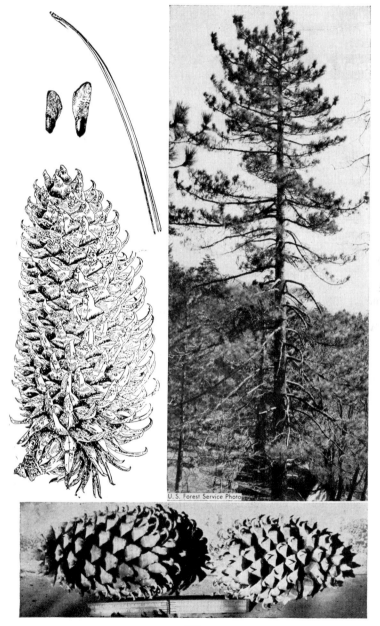

U. S. Forest Service Photo

(Pinus Coulteri)

Usual Occurrence:
> Geographical range—I to L inclusive
> Elevation range   —2,500 to 6,000' (zones 1 and 2)
> Foliage   —Needles, in bundles of 3

Needles: 3 in a bundle, from $6\frac{1}{2}$ to 12" long (average 9"), stiffer and heavier than those of Western Yellow Pine, as are also the branches and twigs.   Needles fall in third or fourth seasons.

Cones:★ 9 to 14" long, very thick and heavy; scales terminating in a broad, incurved, hooked claw $\frac{1}{2}$ to $1\frac{1}{2}$" long, especially at base of cone. The heaviest cones of any American pine; sometimes weigh 4 to 5 lb., green. When falling, cones break through near the base, leaving basal scales on the limb, as do cones of the Yellow Pine.

Bark: Usually $1\frac{1}{2}$ to 2" thick, very dark or blackish brown, roughly broken to form irregular network of longitudinal fissures.

Tree: In maturity $1\frac{1}{2}$ to $2\frac{1}{2}$' × 40 to 60'.   Usually large, long lower branches bend down, often to the ground and have an upward curve at their ends.   Immense bunches of erect, stiff needles form the ends of the branches.

Distribution: Common in the coast ranges of southern and Lower California, 2,500 to 6,000'.   A few trees on the north side of Mt. Diablo (east of San Francisco) mark its northern limit.   Most abundant on San Jacinto and San Bernardino ranges at elevations of about 5,000'.

Other Names: Coulter Pine, Pitch Pine, Nut Pine.

In General: Although it has a general resemblance to young Yellow Pine, this tree is easily distinguished by its heavier masses of foliage, stout twigs, and great cones which are "horribly armed" with talon-like appendages on the scale tips.

Ch25; HH109; J67; Sgt21; Sh2; Su57

(*Pinus flexilis*)

Usual Occurrence:
     Geographical range—B to L inclusive
     Elevation range   —7,000' up (zone 3)
     Foliage   —Needles, in bundles of 5

Needles: In bundles of 5, growing in close masses, often curving, $1\frac{1}{2}$ to 3″ long, on flexible trailing branches. Needles densely clothe ends of the branchlets, forming a sort of brush. Needles are stout, rigid, dark green, deciduous in fifth and sixth years.

Cones: Buff to olive-buff, globose to long ovate. 4 to 10″ long (2 to 5″—J). Require 2 years to mature. By early winter of second year have fallen from the tree. Scar-like umbo. The much-thickened tips of the cone scales are a trait that helps to distinguish this tree from similar species.

Bark: Color of bark on young branches is very light; that on the main stem is 1 to 2″ thick, dark brown, deeply furrowed, and broken crosswise into nearly square plates, covered by small scales.

Tree: Ordinarily 1 to 3′ × 25 to 30′ (2 to 5′ × 40 to 50′—Sgt). Green twigs are so limber★ that they can almost be tied in knots without breaking. Stout, persistent branches ultimately form a wide, round-topped head.

Distribution: Distinctively a tree of the desert ranges, found only at high elevations, usually above 7,000′; in California prefers deserts of high elevation or mountains bordering the desert. Extends east to the Rocky Mountains and ranges from Alberta to New Mexico. Reaches largest size in Arizona and New Mexico.

Other Names: White Pine, Rocky Mountain Pine, Rocky Mountain White Pine (*Pinus strobiformis*), Bull Pine, Arizona Flexilis Pine.

Ch49; HH61; J59; Sgt6; Sh5; Su27

U.S. Forest Service Photo

(*Pinus Balfouriana*)

Usual Occurrence:
       Geographical range—H to K inclusive
       Elevation range   —5,000 to 11,500′ (zone 3)
       Foliage   —Needles, in bundles of 5

Needles: In bundles of 5, from ¾ to 1½″ long, curved and crowded closely to the branch,★ spreading equally all around the branch and massed in "foxtails" near the ends of branches. "Branchlets clothed only at the extremities with long, dense, brushlike masses of foliage." Persist 10 to 15 years.

Cones: Slender when closed, oblong ovate when open, 2½ to 5″ long, 1¾ to 2″ thick. Scales have thick tips with scar-like umbo. (Sargent says "scales armed with minute, incurved prickles.")

Bark: Reddish brown, thin, smoothish but superficially checked into square plates. On old trees sometimes ¾″ thick. Surface scaly.

Tree: In maturity 1 to 3′ × 40 to 60′, rarely 90′. The trunk is stocky and cone-shaped. In old trees trunk axis often projects through crown as dead and shining splinter point. Branches are stout, rather short with half-drooping branchlets.

Distribution: *Spec.* Found at high elevations in small isolated groups usually at or near timberline from Scott Mountains in Siskiyou County to the southern Sierra Nevada on the Kern River watershed. At highest elevations often a low shrub, with wide-spreading, prostrate branches.

Other Names: Balfour Pine.

In General: The name "foxtail" comes from the bushy appearance of the foliage on young branches.

                        Ch45; HH70; J60; Sgt7; Sh5; Su39

U. S. Forest Service Photo

U. S. Forest Service Photo

U.S. Forest Service Photo

(*Pinus monophylla*)

Usual Occurrence:

    Geographical range—I to L inclusive

    Elevation range   —2,500 to 9,000' (zones 2 and 3)

    Foliage   —Needles, attached singly

Needles: Attached singly, occasionally in pairs, 1½ to 2″ long. ★*Perfectly circular* in section, stiff, incurving toward the branch and ending in an abrupt, sharp, prickly tip. Needles are light green and plentiful. Deciduous fourth to twelfth year. Foliage pale yellow-green, with whitish tinge. Faint rib-like grooves lengthwise of the needles.

Cones: Subglobose, 2½ to 3½″ in diameter. Scales thick, raised at ends into high, broad-based pyramids with flattened summits bearing a minute prickle. Seeds in pairs under each seed-bearing scale.

Bark: Dark brown, ¾″ thick, divided by deep irregular fissures into narrow, connected, flat ridges whose surface is broken into thin scales.

Tree: In maturity 12 to 15″ × 15 to 20' (rarely 45'). Trunk often divides near the ground into several spreading stems. The trees are hardly more than bushes, thickset; foliage dense because of the plentiful needles. Appearance suggestive of an old apple tree.

Distribution: Dry desert slopes, some on western slope of Sierra but mainly on east side of the Sierra at elevations of 2,500 to 9,000'. Also Utah, Nevada, Arizona, and Lower California. Common on San Bernardino and San Jacinto Mountains.

Other Names: Piñon, Nut Pine, *Pinus cembroides* var. *monophylla*, Gray Pine, Nevada Nut Pine, One-leaf Piñon.

In General: The only one of the 17 pines of the Pacific slope whose needles are attached singly. Nuts from these trees are the ones sold in stores as "piñon nuts." Cones are gathered when mature but not opened, piled in stacks, and opened by slow fire. An exceedingly slow-growing tree.

Ch61; HH68; J72; Sgt10; Sh5; Su35

U.S. Forest Service Photos

FOURLEAF PINE P-17
(*Pinus cembroides* var. *Parryana*)

Usual Occurrence:
        Geographical range—K and L
        Elevation range   —4,000 to 8,000' (zones 2 and 3)
        Foliage   —Needles, in bundles of 4

Needles:★ In bundles of 1 to 5, usually 4, stout, incurved, pale blue-green with a whitish tinge. ¾ to 1⅝" long. Needles fall in about three years.

Cones: Usually 1¼ to 2¼" long. Very stubby to subglobose.

Bark: Usually ½ to ¾" thick, reddish brown; has wide ridges covered with thick, plate-like scales.

Tree: "Merely a large bush of the desert slopes." A short-trunked, low tree, 15 to 30' high, 10 to 16" in diameter. Thick, spreading branches form a compact crown.

Distribution: Southern and Lower California in dry, mountain regions 4,000 to 8,000'.

Other Names: Nut Pine, Parry Pine, Parry's Nut Pine, Piñon, Parry's Piñon, *Pinus quadrifolia*.

In General: Nuts are used for food, but tree is too scarce to make them an important item in commerce. Young branches are coated at first with a soft, hair-like growth.

Ch65; HH69; J72; Sgt9; Sh5; Su33

Seven species of spruce are native to North America, and five of them are found in forests of the Pacific Coast.

Cones of the spruces mature in one season, are cylindrical or egg-shaped, and always droop from the branches. Most spruces bear their cones at the extreme top of the crown. A distinguishing characteristic of all spruce cones is the thin, papery cone scales, without prickles, very unlike the thick, strong cone scales of most conifers.

Distinguishing traits of spruces as a group are described effectively in a publication of the Canadian Forest Service from which the following quotation is taken:

The spruces can be readily distinguished from all other evergreens by their leaves (needles) which are sharp pointed and usually four sided in cross-section. They are single and stemless and each is borne on a tiny projection on the bark of the twig. In arrangement they are not distinctly two-ranked, as is the rule with the hemlocks and firs, but either bristle out from all sides or, on horizontal branches, are twisted and crowded densely toward the upper side of the twig.

The five species of spruce of which detailed descriptions follow are:

Canadian Forest Service

B. C. Forest Branch Photo

ENGELMANN SPRUCE   S-1

(Picea Engelmannii)

Usual Occurrence:

Geographical range—A to G inclusive

Elevation range   —4,000 to 6,000' in Washington (zones 2 and 3)

Foliage   —Needles, attached singly

Needles: Four-angled, usually about 1″ long, though often longer. They spread spirally on young branchlets that do not bear cones, but on cone-bearing twigs they crowd together upward, brush-like. Soft to the touch. Needle tips are characteristically short and flat. Branchlets are minutely hairy.

Cones: Size varies considerably; length ranges from 1 to almost 3″. Cones grow in large numbers on the upper branches, first horizontally but become pendulous later. Cones are smaller than those of Sitka Spruce and fall in early autumn or winter. "Ends of cone scales are ordinarily squarish, sometimes pointed and notched."—Can

Bark: Scaly even on very young trees. On older trunks it is thin (¼ to ½″ thick) and outwardly composed of very loosely attached scales.

Tree: Mature trees, in dense stands 18 to 36″ × 80 to 100' or more. Larger in open stands, at very high elevations perhaps only 2 to 4' high. Narrow pyramidal crown of small branches. From all main horizontal branches hang numerous tassel-like side branchlets which give the tree a very compact appearance.

Distribution: Alaska southward to northern California—Peace River basin to Colorado, New Mexico, and Arizona. Elevation range:

Canada	1,000 to 6,000'
Washington	4,000 to 6,000'
Arizona	8,500 to 11,000'
Colorado	8,500 to 12,000'

Other Names: Upland Spruce, White Spruce, Western White Spruce, Mountain Spruce, Rocky Mountain Spruce.

In General: A slow-growing tree, very long lived even in unfavorable locations. On high, wind-swept crests specimens only 3 to 5″ in diameter may be 150 to 200 years old. Large trees sometimes 500 to 600 years old. In appearance much similar to Sitka Spruce (S-2).

Although this tree usually grows at higher elevations than Sitka Spruce, the ranges sometimes overlap. Only an expert can distinguish the cones, so careful comparison of needles is necessary for distinction. On this point John A. Lee offers the suggestion: "Cut across several needles with a sharp knife: the section of Engelmann Spruce is distinctly four-angled and square-like while Sitka Spruce has relatively flat needles, less distinctly four-angled."

Can41; HH139; P66; Sgt38; Su78

Ore. Board of Forestry

Chas. Laidlaw Photo

U. S. Forest Service Photo

(Picea sitchensis)

Usual Occurrence:
    Geographical range—A to I inclusive
    Elevation range   —0 to 3,500′ (zone 1)
    Foliage   —Needles, attached singly
  Needles: ½ to 1⅛″ long, flat, sharp pointed, stiff, very indistinctly four-angled,* practically all curved (P). Color, bright yellow-green. Have a bristly habit of standing out at right angles all around branchlets. Prickly to the touch.

  Cones: 2 to 4″ long. Oval, short stalked, hang down conspicuously from the branches. Thin, papery, elliptic scales twice as long as their minutely toothed bracts. Fall every year in the autumn or early winter.

  Bark: Reddish-brown, scaly on very young trees. On large trees, very thin (¼ to ½″ thick); has large, easily detached scales.

  Tree: Mature trees 3 to 6′ × 80 to 125′ (sometimes 12 × 250′—Can). ★Bases of big trunks are swelled by enormous buttresses. In open stands or singly, it has a rapidly tapering bole with branches down to or near the ground. The crown is open, narrow, and sharp in its upper part but very broad at the base where the huge branches are 20 to 30′ long. Small branches lacy. Twigs of the year are always smooth and dark yellow-brown. "The branches are horizontal, frequently with many slender, hanging side-branches."—Can

  Distribution: Northern Alaska to Mendocino County in northern California. Mostly along ocean shoreline only. Maximum distance inland is about 50 miles. Elevation range in Alaska is sea level to 3,500′. (Not above 1,000 or 2,000′ in Oregon.—JL) Contrary to usual custom of conifers, this one attains its highest elevations in the latitudes farthest north.

  Other Names: Coast Spruce, Menzies Spruce, Western Spruce, Tideland Spruce (appropriately suggests the limited inland distribution).

  In General: Noted for longevity. Trees 4 to 6′ × 150 to 180′ are 400 to 750 years old; trees 800 or 850 years old are found occasionally. A leading pulpwood. The largest and most imposing of all the spruces.

  * A needle may be flat and at the same time four-angled if the cross-section has a flattened diamond shape.

Can41; HH137; P43; Sgt41; Sh17; Su81

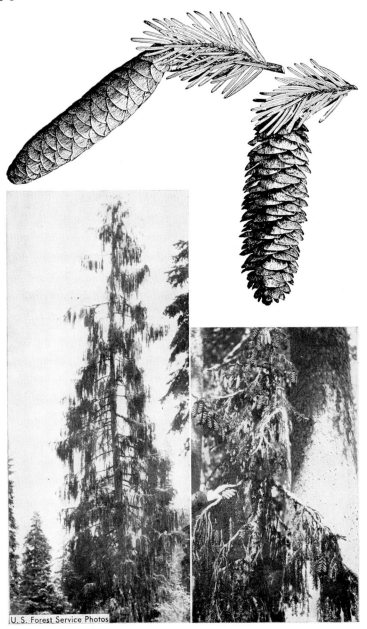

U.S. Forest Service Photos

Usual Occurrence:

Geographical range—G, H

Elevation range   —4,000 to 8,000′ (zones 2 and 3)

Foliage   —Needles, attached singly

Needles: Usually ¾ to 1⅛″ long, attached singly, flat, or obscurely ridged into triangular shape, with the sharpest angle on the lower side.

Cones: About 3 to 3½″ long, ¾ to 1¼″ in diameter. Pendulous from straight, slender stalks. Mature in one season but fall slowly, many persisting until second autumn.

Bark: Dark brown, ¾″ thick; has firmly attached scales.

Tree: In maturity 18 to 30″ × 50 to 75′. Exceptional trees 100′. A thin, spike-like crown bears short, upturned branches. Midway the branches are horizontal, and the ★marked "weeping" habit of its lower branches distinguishes this tree from its associates. Unique characteristic of middle and lower branches is their numerous, very long, string-like branchlets; "slender, flexible, whip-like pendants, often only ¼″ thick and 7 to 8′ long."

Distribution: Southwest Oregon and northern California. Elevation 4,000 to 8,000′.

Other Names: Brewer's Spruce.

In General: A little-known and rare tree. Discovered in 1884.

HH143; Sgt40; Sh17; Su84

U. S. Forest Service Photo

Usual Occurrence:

Geographical range—A

Elevation range   —Sea level to 3,500' (zone 1)

Foliage   —Needles, attached singly

Needles: Needles short and thick ($\frac{1}{4}$ to $\frac{3}{4}$" long), stand out on all sides of branchlets, have blunt tips and a four-angled cross-section. Foliage a deep blue-green, with a whitish tinge.

Cones: Small, only $\frac{1}{2}$ to $1\frac{1}{2}$" long, subglobose. Their habit of remaining ★firmly attached to the branches for very many years (20 or 30 years, sometimes) furnishes one of the most reliable means of distinguishing this species. Stems of the cones are very stout, firm, and curved downward or inward toward the branch. Cone scales are peculiarly stiff and resistant to pressure of the hand but easily broken if squeezed together. Margins of the scales are notched unlike those of the White Spruce, which are smooth.

Bark: Of old trees is thin ($\frac{1}{4}$ to $\frac{1}{2}$"), composed of small, ashy-brown scales.

Tree: In Alaska a small, stunted tree, often only 2 to 6' high, though occasionally 12 to 15' high. (Elsewhere ranges up to 1' in diameter and 50 to 80' high.) Crown characteristically open and irregular, extending to the ground. Branches are short, slim, and often distant from one another.

Distribution: Alaska and northeastern British Columbia (as well as in eastern Canada and the United States). Although essentially a swamp tree in its eastern range, in the North it is found in well-drained valleys and on stony slopes. It associates with Tamarack and Aspen.

Other Names: Red Spruce, Double Spruce, Water Spruce, Swamp Spruce, *Picea nigra*.

In General: This is mainly an eastern and far northern species, included as a Pacific tree only because of its occurrence in the interior of Alaska.

Can35; HH131; Sgt35; Su86

Canadian Forest Service

U. S. Forest Service Photo

(Picea glauca)

Usual Occurrence:

Geographical range—A

Elevation range   —2,000 to 4,000' (zone 2)

Foliage   —Needles, attached singly

Needles: Sharp-pointed, four-angled needles, $\frac{1}{2}$ to $\frac{3}{4}''$ long, stand out all around the twigs except near ends of branchlets where they mass on upper side. Dense foliage, light blue-green color with whitish tinge. Young shoots and needles, when bruised, emit a fetid, skunk-like odor.

Cones: Usual length about $1\frac{3}{4}''$ (range is from 1 to nearly $2\frac{1}{2}''$). Longer ★and more oval-shaped than the Black Spruce, they are pendulous and lightly attached and usually fall in autumn or by spring. When open and dry the cone scales are so thin and flexible that they can be squeezed together without breaking them, and when released they will spring back into place, quite unlike Black Spruce cones in this respect. Although cones are light brown after shedding the seeds, just at maturity they may be light grass-green, tinged with red or bright rose-red.

Bark: $\frac{1}{4}$ to $\frac{1}{2}''$ thick, early broken into small, thin, pale ashy-brown scales.

Tree: In Alaska 12 to $20'' \times 50$ to $75'$ in favorable locations. Also in stunted form only 8 to 20' high. Branches long and thick. Commonly curve downward, then upward. A characteristic is the numerous, small, drooping side branchlets.

Distribution: Newfoundland to Hudson's Bay and northwestward to Alaska, reaching the Pacific at Bering Strait in north latitude 66° 44'. In Alaska at 2,000 to 4,000'. Also down along east side of Rocky Mountains into Montana at elevations of 3,000 to 5,000'.

Other Names: *Picea canadensis, Picea glauca* var. *albertiana*, Single Spruce, Skunk Spruce, Cat Spruce. The last name comes from the odor of young leaves when bruised, which resembles that of the polecat or skunk.

In General: Mainly a tree of the northeastern United States and Canada. Strictly speaking, this is not a tree of the "Pacific slope"; it is included here only because of its range in the interior (at least) of Alaska where it is the principal timber tree in the Yukon drainage basin.

Can36; HH133; Sgt37; Su88

SEQUOIA
SEMPERVIRENS

SEQUOIA
GIGANTEA

DISTRIBUTION MAP
YOSEMITE MUSEUM
U.S.N.P.S.

25 0 25 50 75 100

SCALE-MILES

Only two species now remain of the genus Sequoia, though many more existed in prehistoric times. Remains of at least two Sequoias from which our species descended have been found in fossils of the Cretaceous and Tertiary periods, during which time they lived in the arctic zone. Because of the remarkably fire-resistant quality of the Sequoia bark there has been much speculation as to what caused the extinction of the other species of the family.

Although many of the largest trees have been wholly or partly destroyed, it is believed that *S. gigantea* live 1,000 years longer than the *S. sempervirens*. The sequoias of California are frequently referred to as the oldest living things in the world today. The name comes from an Indian chief, Sequoyah, a Cherokee, inventor of the Cherokee alphabet.

The two species of Sequoia of which detailed descriptions follow are:

Big Tree... Se-1
    (*Sequoia gigantea*)
Redwood.. Se-2
    (*Sequoia sempervirens*)

Se-1

(Sequoia gigantea)

Usual Occurrence:

Geographical range—I, J
Elevation range   —5,000 to 8,500′ (zone 3)
Foliage   —Scale-like

Leaves: Small (⅛ to ¼ or ½″ on leaders), blue-green, awl-shaped, rigid scales which overlap one another and grow in sprays. Small twigs have short leaves; the larger ones have longer leaves; longest of all are the keenly pointed leaves on seedlings one to several years old.

Cones: 2 to 3¾″ long, 1½ to 2¼″ wide. Seeds are thin and flat, four to six under each cone scale. Cones mature the second summer. Seeds ⅛ to ¼″ long.

Bark: 1 to 2′ thick, red, stringy, extremely soft, almost spongy. Composed of fine fibers often frayed out by weather, squirrels, etc.

Tree: In maturity ordinarily 12 to 20′ × 200 to 280′. Some have diameters of 33′ or more. An exaggeration of base diameters is common because of the tendency to include in measurements the immense basal buttresses. In youth the tree forms a broad, sharp-pointed pyramid. After maturity the crown loses all semblance to youthful form and becomes a short, narrow, round-topped dome. Stem often devoid of branches for 150′ or more.

Distribution: *Spec.* Restricted generally to central California. Elevation 5,000 to 8,500′ on west side of the Sierra. (Sudworth lists location of 28 main groves.) See accompanying distribution map.

Other Names: *Sequoia Washingtoniana, Sequoia Wellingtonia,* Giant Sequoia.

In General: Often referred to as the "oldest living thing." Maximum verified life range is about 3,200 years. (Doubtful if any over this age now standing.) Wood and bark contain much tannin, as do drippings from cones which stain water a deep purple. Prostrate trunks lie on the ground for centuries with decay only in the sapwood.

Ch89;FW54;HH189;S30;Sgt62;Sh13;Sul39

Se-1

Geo. J. Young Photo

Dimensions of Largest Living Big Trees

Determining the exact size of the largest living *Sequoia gigantea* was the assignment given to a committee of engineers some years ago by the Junior Chamber of Commerce of Fresno, Calif. The committee made measurements of numerous trees and finally submitted a report which was summarized by J. W. Jourdan, one of the committee, in an article published in *Engineering News-Record*, Feb. 18, 1932, p. 254. The following data are taken from that article.

Each tree was measured to determine (1) the height with reference to a mean base and (2) the restored volume including bark but exclusive of limbs. Restored volume was defined as existing volume plus the quantity lost by burns, the latter being confined largely to the tree bases. A tabular listing of results follows:

COMPARATIVE DIMENSIONS OF FOUR LARGEST BIG TREES

ITEM FOR COMPARISON	NAME OF TREE			
	GEN. SHERMAN	GEN. GRANT	BOOLE	HART
Height of top of trunk, ft..........	272.4	267.4	268.8	277.9
Volume, excluding limbs, cu. ft.....	49,660	43,038	39,974	32,607
Volume of burns, cu. ft............	350	2,194	1,420	1,639
Restored volume, cu. ft............	50,010	45,232	41,394	34,246
Perimeter of base on slope, ft.......	101.6	107.6	112.0	73.8
Perimeter (highest ground), ft......	88.0	92.9	90.3	68.7
Mean diameter of restored base, ft..	30.7	33.3	33.2	26.5
Mean diameter at 60 ft., in ft......	17.5	16.3	15.3	14.5
Mean diameter at 120 ft., in ft.....	17.0	15.0	13.9	12.9
Mean diameter at 180 ft., in ft.....	14.0	12.9	11.9	11.3
Height to first live limb, ft.........	99.7	83.8		
Height to first large limb, ft........	129.9	129.8	126.0	
Diameter first large limb, ft........	6.8	3.2		

Se-1

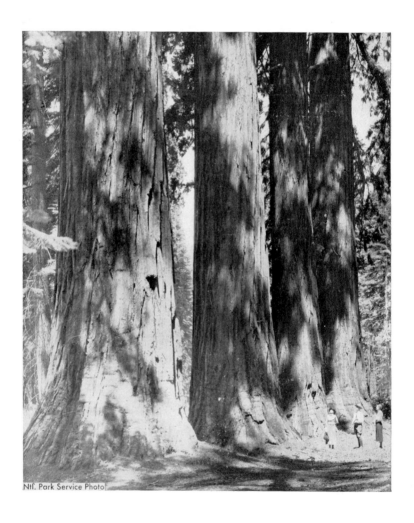

Ntl. Park Service Photo

Additional Notes on the Big Trees

Because this is the most renowned of all California trees, space is devoted here to the following notes abstracted from the book "Big Trees" by Fry and White.

Rate of Growth: Sometimes the annular rings are so closely crowded together that 100 may be counted in a single inch. Again, individual rings may be as much as $\frac{1}{4}''$ thick. Because these trees live where each winter is a snow season and because they grow best when the snows are gone for the summer, it follows that years of greatest growth are years of longest summers, *i.e.*, years when snows melt early.

Other things being equal, this means maximum growth in summers following winters of minimum snowfall. The growing season of these trees may vary from 6 months to as little as 30 days because of temperature (as a factor in snow melting) and other climatic conditions.

Age: It is certain that the Big Tree lives to be 5,000 or 6,000 years old. The chances are overwhelming that they would die from some violent cause (fire, lightning, wind, landslide, etc.) before reaching senescence. In fact there is no record of death of a Big Tree from old age. The oldest ones now living have not lost their power of fertile seed production. Protected in parks they should live 10,000 years, or forever, so far as anyone knows.

Distinction between Big Tree and Redwood: "The chief characteristic of the Redwood is grace—of the Big Tree, majesty."

The foliage, of course, varies widely; the Redwood has needles attached singly, and the Big Tree has scale-like foliage. The Redwood is taller and occurs in heavy forest stands; the Big Tree is larger in diameter; its bark has a richer, deeper color; and most of the trees are in isolated groves. The Redwood grows from seed or from stump sprouts; the Big Tree reproduces only from seed.

Big Tree seed is extremely small—over 3,000 to the ounce. Under natural conditions perhaps only one seed in a million germinates, and a similarly small percentage of those which do germinate take root. Forest fires play an important part in providing likely seeding ground where new trees may start.

Squirrel harvests provide a most convenient source of Big Tree seed. Thirty-eight barley sacks of cones were taken from a single cache made by one squirrel in a 12-day period. These cones yielded 26 lb. of seed.

Fire-resistant Bark: Single fires rarely kill a Big Tree because of the fire resistant bark, but succeeding fires eat away material previously killed by fire. Debris from other trees, more particularly the inflammable, resinous wood of firs and pines, piled about Big Tree bases have caused the greatest fire hazard to this species.

A certain Big Tree 16 ft. in diameter was subjected to a 7-day fire of fir logs on one side of its base. This so "cooked" the wood fibers within the trunk that sap flow was cut off in one-fourth of the sap-flow area. That year the entire tree continued to thrive, living on nourishment within its huge bulk. Next season the topmost 30 ft. died. Thirteen years later a second fire ate away the previously burned portion and reduced the sap-flow area to one-third the original. As a result, in the following season another 15 ft. of the top withered and died. *"Seventy five per cent of dead tops are caused by basal fire scars."*

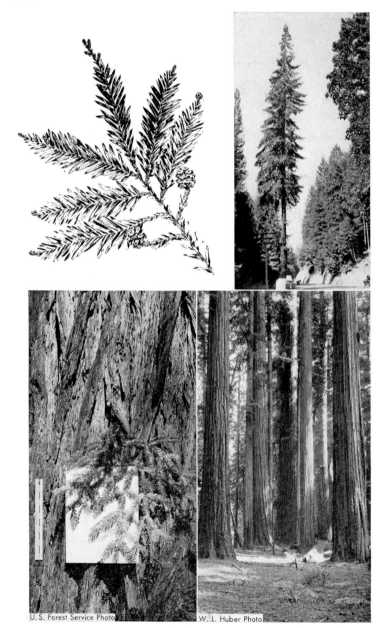

U. S. Forest Service Photo   W. L. Huber Photo

(Sequoia sempervirens)

Usual Occurrence:

    Geographical range—G to J inclusive

    Elevation range   —0 to 3,000' (zone 1)

    Foliage   —Needles, attached singly

Needles: Flat, sharp-pointed, stiff, of unequal length, and lengths of $\frac{1}{3}$ to 1″ may occur on the same twig.   Have a prominent midrib, and show a flat-ranked spray by reason of a half turn at the base.   On side twigs of lower branches and on young saplings, needles stand out in two lines on opposite sides of twig; on the main stems they vary in length down to short scale-like forms, sometimes pressed closely to the branch.   Often cling to branches a year or two after they are dead.   Under sides of needles usually whitish, in contrast with dark green of upper surface.   Needle stems are very short.   Foliage of young growth has a resemblance to Big Tree foliage. Typical sprays are in segments which show annual growth.

    Cones: Even smaller than those of the Big Tree, only $\frac{3}{4}$ to 1″ long.   Seed thin and flat.   Cones mature in one year.   Four or five seeds under each cone scale.

    Bark: Of old trunks 8 to 12″ or more thick, widely furrowed, and ridged at base in rounded, rich brown, stringy strands.

    Tree: In maturity 8 to 12 or 15′ × 190 to 280′.   Sometimes 300′ or more. Grows taller than the Big Tree but has less trunk diameter and is more tapering.

    Distribution: From Chetco River, Oregon (8 miles north of California-Oregon state line), southward to Monterey County, California.   Generally from sea level to about elevation 2,500'.   Mainly on seaward slopes and in fog belt.   Few in Oregon, mainly a California tree.   Shinn says (p. 13): "Habitat is belt 450 mi. long on seaward side Coast Range Mountains from southern Oregon to Santa Lucia Mountains in Monterey County.   Greatest distance inland, 30 mi.   Never grows naturally out of reach of the ocean fogs."   See accompanying distribution map.

    Other Names: Coast Redwood.

    In General: Age average is much less than the Big Tree.   A Redwood 20′ in diameter and 350′ high gave a ring count of 1,000.   Oldest ring count about 2,300 years.

HH185;P65;S19;Sgt61;Sh13;Sul45

About 1932 the California Park Board commissioned E. P. French, superintendent of the northwest district, to make a search for the tallest tree in the redwood belt. After several months, during which he measured hundreds of trees, French reported that a tree at Dyerville measuring 364' high was the tallest. This tree now is known as the "Founders Tree" in honor of Dr. John C. Merriam, Madison Grant, and Dr. Henry Fairfield Osborn, founders of the "Save the Redwoods League." Dimensions of other large Redwoods are given in the table.

DIMENSIONS OF LARGE REDWOODS
(Data from California State Division of Parks, Sept. 4, 1937)

LOCATION	CIRCUM-FER-ENCE ON GROUND	DIAM-ETER BREAST HIGH	HEIGHT, FT.	TIMBER, FT., BOARD MEASURE	
				STAND	MILL CUT
Del Norte State Park (Stout Memorial Grove)........	62' 3"	16' 6"	340	....	130,800
Humboldt State Park (¾ mile north of Elk Grove Camp, on Prairie Creek).	90'	17' 7"	200	....	128,000
Bull Creek Flat (4 miles west of Dyerville).......	72'	16' 6"	345	235,000	154,000
Dyerville Flat (tallest Redwood).................	47'	....	364	....	125,000
California Redwood Park:					
Father Tree............	66' 9"	16' 10"	250	177,000	133,000
Mother Tree...........	70'	15' 3"	329	141,345	101,960
Santa Clara Tree........	65' 6"	17' 9"	240	200,000	145,000
North of Klamath-Coulter (tree advertised as world's largest)................	71'	16' 2"	280	....	84,000

To

CALIFORNIA NUTMEG   To

*(Torreya californica)**

Usual Occurrence:
    Geographical range—H, to K inclusive
    Elevation range   —0 to 6,000' (zones 1 and 2)
    Foliage   —Needles, attached singly

Needles: Flat, shining, sharply pointed, rigid, 1¼ to 3″ long. Needles attach uniformly to branchlets so as to form a two-ranked, flat spray. Lustrous on upper surface, paler green to whitish below.

Fruit: The seed kernel suggests the nutmeg of commerce (also resembles olive or small plum), green in color when ripe, streaked with purple. 1⅛ to 1¾″ long. Shell of seed longitudinally grooved.

Bark: ⅓ to ½″ thick, rather soft, finely checked seams, green on the younger branches but yellows with age. Sometimes gray-brown, tinged with orange. Elongated, loose scales are common.

Tree: In maturity 1½ to 3′ × 15 to 50′, rarely 4 × 100′. Slender branches stand out rather straight from the trunk in formal circles and are somewhat drooping at their extremities. Trunks are rarely straight, in maturity are clear of branches for two-thirds of the height.

Distribution: *Spec.* On west slopes of the Sierra and in the Coast Range. From Lake and Mendocino Counties on the north to Kern County on the south, but never in any considerable quantity. Prefers cool, shady canyons or sheltered slopes. On western slopes of the Sierra usual elevation range is 3,000 to 5,000'; along the coast the elevation range extends down to sea level.

Other Names: Yew, Stinking Yew, Stinking Cedar, Nutmeg Tree, California False Nutmeg, *Tumion Californicum.*

In General: A rare tree, called "Nutmeg" from the fancied resemblance of its seed kernels to the nutmeg of commerce, which belongs to a different and unrelated family of broadleaf plants. ★A sharp, aromatic, and disagreeable odor is emitted by needles or branchlets when bruised; hence the name "Stinking Cedar." Not a cone bearer, but included here because it is likely to be mistaken for one.

* Not a cone bearer.

HH226; J127; Sgt92; Sh17; Su191

U.S. Forest Service Photo   Geo. D. Whittle Photo

(Taxus brevifolia)*

Usual Occurrence:

 Geographical range—A to I inclusive

 Elevation range —0 to 6,000' (zones 1, 2, and 3)

 Foliage   —Needles attached singly

Needles: $\frac{1}{2}$ to 1″ long about $\frac{1}{16}$″ wide; flat, rounded ends; deep, yellow-green above; paler below. Soft to the touch, have stout midribs. Persistent 5 to 12 years.

Fruit: This species does not bear cones but has a small, bright red fruit about $\frac{1}{3}$″ long which is palatable and often is eaten by birds. The fruit resembles the red huckleberry, but the seed protrudes from the fleshy covering and always is on the underside of branchlets.

Bark: About $\frac{1}{4}$″ thick, composed of papery, purple, easily detached scales. Beneath the scales the newer bark is clear rose-red or purple-red.

Tree: In maturity 6 to 12″ × 20 to 30' (rarely 80'). Inland, away from the coast, the tendency is to smaller size; sometimes shrubby. Trunks are straight and fluted by an apparent infolding of the surface, frequently unsymmetrical, one diameter much exceeding the other. Slender branches, straight, somewhat drooping. Very slender branchlets hang down giving a weeping appearance.

Distribution: Along the coast ranges from Alaska to central California, eastward to Montana. Grows in moist locations. Found near Monterey Bay and on western slopes of Sierra Nevada. Elevation range in California is sea level to 6,000'.

Other Names: Yew, Pacific Yew, Mountain Mahogany.

In General: Not a cone bearer, but included here because it is likely to be mistaken for one.

* Not a cone bearer.

Can72; HH228; P66; Sgt93; Sh17; Su194

GLOSSARY

bole—the main trunk or stem of a tree.

bract—a modified or undeveloped leaf or organ attached to or between the scales of cones.

catkin—a densely flowered, scaly spike which falls whole after flowering or after maturity. Also applied to flowering cones.

crown—the branches and foliage of a tree or shrub. As used in describing the appearance of the tree as a whole, it means the entire tree above the base of the trunk.

dendrology—the branch of botany dealing with trees.

glaucous—overcast with a whitish bloom, as on a plum.

glandular—provided with gland-like protuberances on the surface or partly imbedded in the surface.

globose—globular, or nearly so.

morphology—the branch of biology dealing with the form and structure of animals and plants.

ovate⎫
ovoid⎭—broad and tapering to a narrow apex, egg-shaped.

ovule—the part of the flower that becomes a seed.

silva—the forest trees of a region collectively.

stomata—breathing pores in the epidermis of needles connecting internal cavities with the external air.

subglobose—somewhat less rounded than would justify the term globose.

umbo—a certain protuberance or point. Here applied to formations on the tips of cone scales.

whorl—radial from a common point. A circle of flowers, branches or other growths about the same point on the axis, like the spokes of a wheel around the hub.

Because of the very frequent use of the word "species" in this manual the beginner may find it helpful if the distinctions between genus, species, and variety are made clear so that he will not misuse or confuse these terms.

A *genus* is a group of one or more related species classified separately because this group differs from other groups in a fundamental way.

A *species* is a group of lower order than a genus and refers to a single distinct type, *i.e.*, trees that have distinctive characteristics in common.

A *variety* is a group of lower order than a species, indicating relation by descent and distinction from similar groups only by traits too slight to constitute a separate species.

These definitions will become clearer from the following statements: The genus pine includes many species such as Yellow Pine and Sugar Pine, and among these species are some in which there are more than one variety. For example, some authors distinguish the beach variety of Lodgepole Pine (P-4) from the mountain variety. Both varieties belong to the species Lodgepole Pine which is one of the many species included in the genus "pine."

INDEX

(Symbols, alphabetically arranged, are used in place of page numbers)